Alex J. Szecsody

Random Noise and Vibration in Space Vehicles

Richard H. Lyon
Bolt Beranek and Newman Inc.

1967

The Shock and Vibration Information Center
United States Department of Defense

For sale by the Superintendent of Documents, U.S. Government Printing Office
Washington, D.C. 20402 - Price $1.50

Contract No. N00014-66-C0271

Library of Congress Catalog Card No. 67-62274

The Shock and Vibration Monograph Series

The Shock and Vibration Information Center has instituted this monograph series to provide state-of-the-art reports in specialized areas within its general field of interest — mechanical shock and vibration. These reports are prepared by recognized authorities judged well qualified to summarize the work already done and to identify areas needing further study.

The approach prescribed in preparing the monographs is first to obtain the existing literature pertaining to the particular topic. Then this literature is evaluated, and a critical review is written. Finally, conclusions are drawn as to the present standing of the technology and the gaps that exist. Each monograph is accompanied by a detailed bibliography.

The number of topics treated is necessarily limited by available funds and time. It is hoped that the results of the efforts on those topics selected will prove useful to the scientific community we serve.

This monograph is available to qualified users from the Defense Documentation Center, Cameron Station, Alexandria, Virginia 22314. Others may purchase it from the Superintendent of Documents, U.S. Government Printing Office, Washington, D.C. 20402.

The Shock and Vibration Information Center

William W. Mutch, Head

Henry C. Pusey

Rudolph H. Volin

Jean B. Goldbecker, Editor

Katherine G. Jahnel, Administrative Secretary

TABLE OF CONTENTS

CHAPTER 1
INTRODUCTION

It is the purpose of this monograph to present a critical review of the ability of the engineering profession to anticipate the dynamic environment of a flight vehicle, to predict the vehicle response to this environment, and to simulate the expected environment in the laboratory. The ability to do these things has progressed significantly in the last few years, although engineering practice has not completely kept up with the rapidly advancing technology. It is hoped that this monograph will aid in spreading this new information to a larger group of environmental engineers.

Many of the methods described in the following chapters will rely on arguments motivated on physical grounds as well as on mathematical models of the environment and the structure. Environmental engineers have generally taken the attitude that predictions of response must be made, even in the face of imperfect data and methods. For this reason some empiricism is evident in the arguments. Empiricism is frequently useful because of the economics of effort that can result from simple rule-of-thumb procedures.

Generally, the studies that we report on are applicable to sustained loads that are random in time but may or may not be spatially homogeneous. We exclude by implication, therefore, such loads as pyrotechnic shock and combustion or structural-propulsion interaction instabilities. In certain cases, it is possible to treat these loads by statistical methods, but the appropriate conditions require experience and judgment for their application.

The following paragraphs describe briefly the subject matter of the book. In that sense they serve as an outline. Their primary purpose, however, is to make explicit the interconnecting ideas and the logical relationships within the material to be covered.

1.1 Prediction of the Environment

In the totality of the environmental problem comprising prediction of loads, calculation of response, and design of simulation, the loads prediction problem is by far the least advanced. In part, this is due to our inability to predict flow behavior from the Navier-Stokes equation [1].* It is also due to the multitude of different but significant loads—acoustic, turbulent boundary layer, wake

---

*References are cited in the Bibliography, appendix B.

1

impingement, oscillating shocks, separated flows, etc. [2]—that are experienced by the vehicle. These loads appear on a vehicle at different places during different periods of its trajectory and their intensity and excitation characteristics depend on both trajectory and geometric parameters [2, Sect. 2].

There are three ways that information on loads is obtained: through theoretical computation, laboratory studies on models, and flight measurements on vehicles. As a practical matter, a particular estimate is often a combination of all three methods. Theoretical and laboratory studies suggest general features such as overall levels, spectral shapes and scaling laws, while flight measurements on similar vehicles serve to corroborate these studies and to indicate the kinds of loads that may be present [3].

The equations governing structural motion require considerable detail in specifying the applied loads, either in terms of pressure as a function of time at all positions on the surface, or by statistics of the pressure such as the space-time covariance [4]. Since only a limited number of measurements can be practicably obtained in laboratory or flight studies, it is necessary to develop conceptual models of the environment. These are fitted to the expected environment by laboratory and field measurements, but they always imply more (and less) detail than can be justified from the data [5]. We shall explore this point more fully in the discussions to come.

In summary, it is possible at present to give a description of the dynamic environment for a particular vehicle in a given trajectory. This description will have its weak points, and much work is required to improve it, but it can serve as a basis for response calculations. We turn to that subject now.

1.2 Calculation of Response

An aerospace flight vehicle is a very complicated structure, consisting of the outer skin, frames and stingers, and internal structure and acoustic spaces. In quite a real sense, it defies description, except perhaps through the library of technical drawings used in the specification of its construction. Even if one had an exact mechanical description of the structure, however, with every rivet and weld exactly positioned and defined, and a magnificent computer able to contain all of the structural and environmental data, then one could still be dissatisfied with solutions of response obtained.

The development of scientific or engineering understanding of a system is closely related to one's ability to reduce the system to simpler elements. To the extent that one can identify certain response characteristics as due to *cylinder behavior,* or *panel modes,* or *fluid loading,* it is possible to predict how the response might be changed by changing appropriate properties of the structure [2, Sect. 3].

In the following discussions, the methods for computing response are classified in accordance with the way that the structure is modeled. A given structure can be modeled in several ways, depending on the frequency of response and the kind of excitation. It is the engineer's job to pick the proper structural and environmental model for the calculation of response.

By and large, the models ignore effects of nonlinearity in response [6]. A major distinction can also be drawn between models that are infinite in extent, and those that are finite. The former generally require calculation of *traveling wave* response, while the response of the latter is expressed as vibration of normal modes. In many cases it is possible to obtain equivalent results from these apparently quite different systems.

The major purpose of the structural model is to predict the excitation of that part of the structure directly exposed to the environment. Frequently, however, one is also concerned about mechanical and acoustic energy transmitted to interior portions of the vehicle [7]. Structural models for transmission generally require a more subtle design than those designed for response only. The difference lies in the role of *nonresonant* motion, which must be adequately represented in transmission studies [8]. We shall discuss a model for both sound and vibration transmission in chapter 3.

Finally, we must recognize the role of laboratory and field studies in response estimation. In fact, much of the current estimation of environmental response is based on purely empirical understanding. Only recently have analytical methods become capable of providing a reasonable alternative (or complement) to the purely empirical procedures [2].

1.3 Simulation of Environmental Loads

The simulation of a load is the replacement of that load by another designed to be equivalent to it in some sense. The simulation may attempt to copy the service load; e.g., a turbulent boundary layer (TBL) on a flight vehicle may be simulated by a TBL in a wind tunnel model [9]. The simulation may replace one load with another: acoustic-induced vibration in a service vehicle may be simulated by shaker-induced vibration in the laboratory [10]. Whatever the method, it is desirable that a good understanding be achieved of the phenomenon that is being simulated.

Suppose we are interested in the noise generated within a spacecraft shroud during the high-Q portion of its trajectory. Let us further suppose that the shroud vibration had been monitored during this portion of the flight. If the same vibration levels are induced in the shroud by placing it in an acoustic chamber (and thereby assuming an equivalence between aerodynamic and acoustic response), then it may happen that the sound levels within the shroud are not correctly reproduced [11].

When service acoustic loads are simulated by sound fields in the laboratory, then relatively simple scaling laws are operative. The scaling laws for some aerodynamic loads such as separated flows and oscillating shocks are more difficult to demonstrate. In these cases, it is necessary to rely heavily on data taken over a range of scale factors in order to demonstrate that extrapolation is reasonable. Examples of such extrapolation will be given [12].

The principal point to be made is that simulation must be carried out with great care and with understanding of its purpose and limitations. Both environmental and structural parameters will affect the success of a simulation. Scaled attempts to replace a flight environment with a wind tunnel experiment may be quite misleading, while another test of panel response to an oscillating shock might be quite well simulated with a mechanical shaker. It is only required that one understand the system sufficiently well. How well the systems are understood that we are considering will be revealed in the following.

CHAPTER 2
FLIGHT VEHICLE NOISE ENVIRONMENT

In this chapter, we consider several aspects of the noise environment of flight vehicles: what the major types of environment are, how they are measured, when they may be expected, and how we are to estimate the intensity of each kind of environment.

The kinds of environment are first separated into *acoustic* and *aerodynamic*. By acoustic, we mean pressure fluctuations that propagate with the speed of sound and are related to velocity fluctuations by the formulas of ordinary acoustic theory. Aerodynamic noise is a broader term, encompassing pressure loads due to turbulence and shock waves. In the present context, it includes turbulent boundary layers, separated flow, wake flow, base pressure fluctuations, and oscillating shocks.

The reason for an environmental estimate is primarily response estimation or simulation. Calculations of response require considerable information regarding the temporal and spatial characteristics of the loads—more information than is generally available from flight measurements. The needed information is usually inferred by fitting the data to an assumed model of the load, a model that may be established from laboratory studies. Insofar as possible, we shall try to indicate in the following just how well the various environmental models are established by laboratory and field data.

2.1 Acoustic Environment

The acoustic environment of a flight vehicle is generated by the engines, by flow over the vehicle structure, and by moving parts of the vehicle, such as propellers. The sound generated by propellers, rotating helicopter blades, and the compressor blades associated with bypass jet engines is now reasonably well understood. Noise from this source is generally of concern from the community reaction viewpoint and is not important as a structural load [13]. The noise caused by flow over the structure is of great interest in terms of cabin noise levels (which we cover in sections on response to aerodynamic noise). In at least one rather special case, the anticipated sound levels radiated onto a laminar wing by turbulence is of interest since the laminar boundary layer on such an airfoil might be quite sensitive to noise [14]. For this report, we shall concentrate on the broadband sound radiated by subsonic and supersonic jet and rocket engines.

5

Subsonic Jet Noise

The primary interest in the jet noise of aircraft has been the radiation of sound away from the vehicle [15] because this noise is troublesome to the community. Fortunately, the characteristics of the engine as a source of community noise can be fairly easily summarized. They have to do with overall power, directivity, and spectra as these are related to engine power and geometry [16]. Unhappily, the loads that the engine noise places on the vehicle are not so simply related to these parameters, but depend on details of the vehicle and engine configuration in a fairly complicated way.

The long-range propagation of engine noise has been reasonably well documented, and will not be pursued here. There has also been a fair amount of work on the structural loads induced by subsonic jets; some of it is documented in the open literature, but much of it resides in the data files of airframe manufacturers. The structural loads are reviewed in the following paragraphs.

The determination of acoustic loads for airframe applications is perhaps best exemplified by the work of Clarkson. In two particular studies, on the geometric zone pressure field of the Comet engine [17, p. 22] and in a mockup of the Caravelle tail section [17, p. 27], Clarkson has obtained data on the scaling laws for pressure correlations between jets of varying sizes. Using these correlations, he has also been able to determine the boundary between the nonradiated hydrodynamic field of the jet and the geometric field.

The induction (hydrodynamic) field of the subsonic jet extends about 2 diameters outward from the jet boundary. In this region, correlation patterns of pressure are similar to those of boundary layer pressure fluctuation, except that the dependence of convection velocity on frequency is much greater, the dependence being approximately

$$U_c \sim f^{1/2}.$$

This is a much stronger relationship than similar ones derived for a turbulent boundary layer [18].

The intensity and spectra of pressure fluctuations in the induction and geometric fields have not been fully studied. Most workers assume that the induction field is proportional to the dynamic pressure of the jet,

$$p_{ind} \sim q_{jet},$$

and that the rms pressure in the geometric field [19] (which extends outward about 10 diameters from the jet boundary and 20 diameters downstream) varies with jet parameters in the same way that the far-field radiation does. These regions are summarized in Fig. 1.

In the subsonic jet, the total radiated power rises as a very high power of the jet efflux velocity U. If the jet is relatively clean aerodynamically, the law is

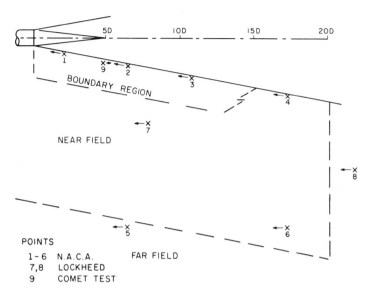

Fig. 1. Sketch of zone geometry for subsonic jet, showing induction, Fresnel and fraunhofer radiation regions [17].*

$$\Pi_{rad} \simeq 6 \times 10^{-5}\rho D^2 U^8/c^5, \qquad (2.1)$$

where ρ is the density of gas in the jet, D is the nozzle diameter, and c is the speed of sound in the surrounding medium.

The spectrum of overall radiated power is shown in Fig. 2 [16]. The spectrum can generally be normalized by a Strouhal frequency U/D. Thus, the geometric field magnitude and spectrum can usually be adjusted to predict the sound from jets having differing efflux velocities and sizes, providing that they are subsonic, "clean," and that one is comparing spectra at geometrically similar observation positions.

Supersonic Jets

When the flow issuing from the jet nozzle is faster than the speed of sound in the surrounding medium, the efficiency of the turbulence sound sources will be increased. If the jet is hot, as it usually is in cases of interest for jet-powered vehicles, the flow can be subsonic with respect to the jet itself, but supersonic with respect to the ambient air. In this case, the flow in the jet will decelerate smoothly. When the flow in the jet is also supersonic with respect to itself, then strong shocks may occur as it decelerates.

*Figure 1 in "Scaling of the Near Field Pressure Correlation Patterns around a Jet Exhaust," by B. L. Clarkson, in *Acoustical Fatigue in Aerospace Structures,* edited by Walter J. Trapp and Donald M. Forney, Jr. Copyright © 1965 by Syracuse University Press, Syracuse, New York. By permission of the publisher.

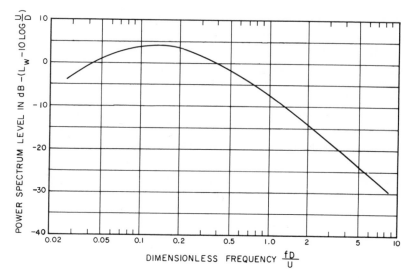

Fig. 2. Normalized power spectrum for subsonic jets [16].

Figure 3 is a Schlieren photograph of a supersonic jet showing a complicated pattern of sound emission from the supersonic region as Mach wavelets, from the shock region, and from the subsonic region. The relative strength of each portion of the jet as a source region remains to be clarified, as does the nature of the sources. Nevertheless, a fair amount of data has been collected from jet and rocket engine firings, and it will be useful to review some of these and how they are applied to define environmental levels.

Early studies of model supersonic jets were carried out for the purposes of understanding their noise production—how the frequency spectra of radiated power scale with efflux velocity and jet diameter, how the overall radiated power relates to jet power, and how the distribution of radiated power depends on the angle from the jet axis. For these purposes, the measurement of noise pressures in the neighborhood of the jet—whether they be the nonradiated induction field or the radiated but complex geometric field (or Fresnel zone)—represents an unnecessary complication. Thus, much of the information on *rocket noise* is of little value in estimating the loads on the launch vehicle or other nearby structures.

We can see examples of this by comparing estimates of rocket noise on a vehicle with published data on flight vehicles. An early estimate of vehicle environment was given by Bies and Franken [20]. They also extrapolated far-field measurements to the vehicle locations. In general, these estimates predict a frequency maximum in the excitation that is too low. They also tend to be rather low in amplitude.

A revision to the early estimates was made in 1963 by Franken and Wiener [21]. This procedure was based on measurements of acoustic spectra on launch vehicles—Jupiter, Atlas, Titan, and Saturn I static firings. More recent data on Saturn launch vehicles tend to confirm the general features of the latter estimates, except that (a) the levels do not diminish as quickly as anticipated as one proceeds from the booster to the payload sections and (b) the spectrum does not undergo, in the same progression, as large a shift to lower frequencies as anticipated.

The conclusion that one is forced to draw from the foregoing is that reasonable estimates of vehicle loads due to acoustic noise from its jets, subsonic or supersonic, must at present be based on direct measurements of the loads on similar or scaled vehicles. Theoretical notions of sound generation and propagation are useful as guides to scaling the frequency scale and overall level, but they are of little value at present in predicting the levels on a new vehicle configuration.

This rather empirical state of affairs in acoustic load estimation is repeated when one considers the other flight loads—TBL, separated flows, wakes, base pressure fluctuations, oscillating shocks, etc. Paradoxically, however, the extrapolation of laboratory and field data to new situations for these loads is more straightforward than for the sound field, although this may be an illusion maintained by the paucity of published data on aerodynamic loads.

NASA Langley Research Center photograph.

Fig. 3. Supersonic jet showing Mach wave formation.

2.2 Inertial Aerodynamic Loads

The aerodynamic loads that we shall discuss are due essentially to the forward motion of the vehicle and may be broadly categorized into two classes. The first we term inertially induced; these tend to be proportional to the dynamic head of the flow about the vehicle. Examples are the TBL, separated and wake flows and base pressure fluctuations. The second class of loads is compressibility induced. Examples of these are transonic and supersonic oscillating shocks and cavity resonances.

Based on wind tunnel observations and flight data, the locations and magnitudes of the major fluctuating aerodynamic environments are fairly well known. A summary of these environments and their occurrence as a function of geometry and speed is shown in Fig. 4.

An attached TBL is a major environment over large parts of the vehicle for a substantial portion of the atmospheric flight profile. This is true for both aircraft and spacecraft. The prediction of the TBL load is largely empirical and is based on wind tunnel data and flight data for both aircraft and spacecraft. A recent report by Bies [22] summarizes much of the available TBL pressure data for aircraft, spacecraft, and wind tunnels. In a subsonic wind tunnel, the overall fluctuating pressure coefficient C_{prms} is nearly

$$C_{prms} = \frac{p_{rms}}{\frac{1}{2}\rho V^2} = 0.006. \qquad (2.2)$$

As the Mach number increases, this coefficient tends to decrease, and for Reynolds numbers greater than 10^7 (based on distance from the leading edge), the reduction is nearly 10 dB by the time the Mach number has increased to 3 or 4.

The fluctuation pressure coefficients for aircraft in regions of smooth flow appear to be equal to those for flat plates in wind tunnels. For spacecraft, there are reasons where the flow is disturbed, but not separated. In such regions we may therefore prefer to use the coefficient

$$C_{prms} = 0.02. \qquad (2.3)$$

Additional flight data will improve estimates of these parameters, but these will serve satisfactorily for most purposes.

The overall pressure fluctuation is of interest but it must be supplemented by a knowledge of the spatial and temporal correlations (or spectra) in order to predict response. To convert from the fixed-position single microphone measurement to a determination of the correlation, a model of the pressure correlations must be assumed. A particular model of the correlation that has enjoyed wide usage is the following [23]:

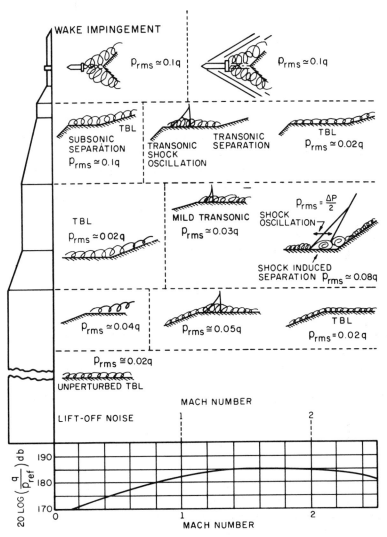

Fig. 4. Fluctuating aerodynamic loads depending on vehicle location and Mach number [2].

$$\langle p(x,t)p(x',t')\rangle = \langle p^2\rangle\phi_p(\xi_1,\xi_3,t)$$
$$= \langle p^2\rangle\phi_1(\xi_1 - U_c\tau)\phi_3(\xi_3)\phi_m(\tau) \qquad (2.4)$$

where $\xi_1 = x_1 - x'_1$, $\xi_3 = x_3 - x'_3$, $\tau = t - t'$. Equation (2.4) represents a correlation field, convected in the x_1 (downstream) direction at a speed U_c and changing in time so that the temporal correlation in this moving frame is $\phi_m(\tau)$. The change in correlation as one traverses across the flow is given by ϕ_3.

The form of Eq. (2.4) is a reflection of the way in which TBL pressure data are analyzed. A measurement of the autocorrelation at one point is given by setting $\xi_1 = \xi_3 = 0$:

$$\phi_p(\tau) = \phi_1(U_c\tau)\phi_m(\tau). \tag{2.5}$$

It is usually assumed, on the basis of empirical evidence, that $\phi_m(\tau)$ is much more slowly varying than is ϕ_1. Thus, at least for small values of ξ_1 (or $U_c\tau$), the fixed microphone measurement ϕ_p gives a good indication of the form of ϕ_1. It is usually a function that decays rapidly in space and becomes negative for large values of the argument. There has been a long standing discussion among fluid dynamicists as to whether or not the integral $\int_0^\infty \phi_1(\xi)d\xi$ has a non-zero value, but it is a point of relatively small importance for structural response [24].

The *transverse* spatial correlation $\phi_3(\xi_3)$ may be measured by setting $\tau = 0$ and $\xi_1 = 0$, and measuring the spatial crosscorrelation transverse to the direction of flow. In this case, there is fairly good correlation of results between experimenters, all of them more or less agreeing on the form [5; 23, p. 15]:

$$\phi_3(\xi_3) = \exp\left[-\xi_3/L_3\right]. \tag{2.6}$$

There are also data taken on the more general correlation $\phi_p(\xi_1, \xi_3, 0)$. It does not completely support the factoring of the spatial correlation into separate downstream and cross-stream components. Almost all applications of loads information at the present time do assume, however, that this factorization can be carried out [25].

The experimental determination of $\phi_m(\tau)$ is suggested by Eq. (2.4). Since $\phi_1(0) = \phi_3(0) = 1$, ϕ_m can be found from

$$\phi_m(\tau) = \phi_p(\xi_1 = U_c\tau, \xi_3 = 0, \tau). \tag{2.7}$$

The experimental process consists of generating a series of curves $\phi_p(\xi_1, 0, \tau)$, where ξ_1 is a fixed parameter and τ is the abscissa. The function $\phi_m(\tau)$ is the envelope of these curves, and the convection speed is the ratio of the ξ value for any particular curve to the time delay τ at the tangent point [26].

The preceding discussion is oversimplified, as anyone who has made such experiments can testify. In fact, the values of convection speed as obtained for the different values of ξ_1 will vary and the shape of ϕ_p will change as a function of τ in a way that is not totally explainable from the shape of the modulation $\phi_m(\tau)$. Much time and effort have gone into trying to get better correlation models, and with some success. Let us note, however, that environmental estimation is a systems problem. It has not been demonstrated that many of the finer points in the correlation determinations have any significant effect on structural response, and in some cases, one can demonstrate that there is very little effect [23, Fig. 1]. An example is the insensitivity of response of a high-speed vehicle to the moving axis temporal correlation.

The estimation of TBL loads relies heavily on wind tunnel measurements, but increasingly, flight data are also playing a part in the loads estimates. By far, the bulk of the data is of single-microphone temporal autocorrelations or of its frequency transform, the power spectral density (PSD). In a few cases, spatial crosscorrelations have been measured, and in general, they support the conclusions drawn from the wind tunnel measurements, except for the increase in overall level as noted above. Flight data have been obtained on a glider wing [27], on commercial [28] and military aircraft [29], and for spacecraft [30], launch vehicles [31] and experimental military payloads [32]. The TBL environment can be summarized as follows:

1. The overall fluctuating pressure varies with dynamic head and Mach number, from approximately $0.02Q$ at M = 1 to 0.006 at M = 4 for spacecraft and 0.006 for aircraft. The mission profile will determine the coefficient appropriate to the period of high TBL excitation.

2. The pressure disturbances are convected along the vehicle surface at 60 to 80 percent of the local free-stream flow speed.

3. The spatial scale of the disturbance in both the down- and cross-stream directions is approximately δ^*, where δ^* is the displacement thickness of the boundary layer. The actual spectra of ϕ_1 and ϕ_3 are required for response estimations, and these have the fairly universal forms shown in Figs. 5 and 6.

Separated Flows

Separated flow fields, when they occur on a flexible structural surface, can produce a significant part of the response due to the fluctuating pressure environment. In this category we can place wakes from protuberances and other nonfaired structural elements on the forward parts of the vehicle, shock-induced separation on transonic and supersonic vehicles near places where there is a rapid rate of change of vehicle cross-sectional area, and stalled flow regions such as at base separation or on separation airfoils at large angles of attack.

In the following chapter, we discuss methods for using loads information to estimate structural response. Suffice it to say here that, in general, the ratio of response to excitation in any frequency band depends on the type of excitation. A particular pressure PSD measured at a position on the structure will produce differing response PSD's if the pressure is due to a sound field or if it arises from a TBL. We must, therefore, know more than the PSD—we must know what kind of flow induces that pressure field before we can calculate response. Unfortunately, only a very few correlation studies have been made for separated flows. A greater degree of guesswork (the euphemism is extrapolation) is required in the response computation than when the excitation arises from an acoustic field or a TBL.

A useful and simple assumption is that a region of separated or wake flow is like a very thick TBL, with a convection speed approximately 50 to 60 percent of the free stream (or vehicle) speed [2]. The intensity of the pressure

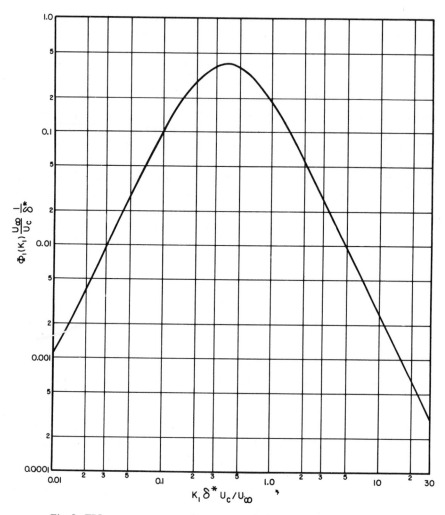

Fig. 5. TBL pressure wave number spectrum in downstream direction [23].

fluctuations in separated regions on the forward part of the vehicle associated with transonic and supersonic shocks is approximately [2]

$$p_{rms} \simeq 0.05Q. \tag{2.8}$$

In regions where wake flow impinges on the vehicle, the pressure is more nearly [2]

$$p_{rms} \simeq 0.1Q. \tag{2.9}$$

There have been some measurements of both pressure fluctuation and correlation for separated flow over a delta wing aircraft at Southampton [33]. In this case, the overall pressure fluctuation was nearly

$$p_{rms} \simeq 0.02Q. \tag{2.10}$$

The pressure fluctuations did show a convection effect, but the convection had a large component transverse to the main direction of flow.

For purposes of response estimation, one can assume that the convected loads due to separated flows are completely analogous to a TBL with a larger characteristic dimension. For a wake, the radius dimension of the obstacle producing

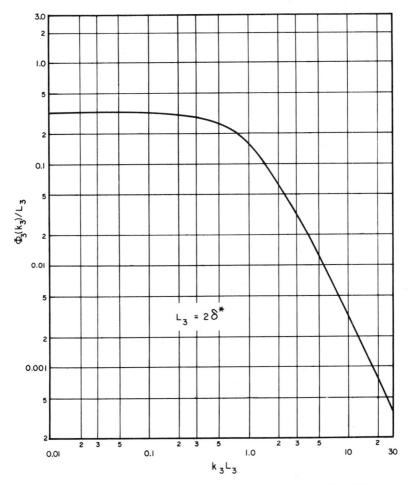

Fig. 6. TBL pressure wave number spectrum in cross-stream direction [23].

the wake may take the place of the displacement thickness δ^*. In supersonic or transonic shock-induced separation, it is a multiple of the displacement thickness of the incoming TBL—the factor is usually 2 or 3 [2].

At the base of the vehicle, or at a more forward part of the vehicle that is strongly reentrant, strong flow separation is also accompanied by pressure fluctuations. Such loads are called *base pressure fluctuations* (BPF). Unfortunately, the only data existing give only PSD information for a single microphone sensor [34]. There is essentially no information available, therefore, on the spatial correlation or the presence (or absence) of convection effects. Also, the data are for a subsonic case. These data do suggest, however, two important features of this environment. First, the overall pressure fluctuations are closer in magnitude to the attached TBL (Eq. 2.3) rather than the separated flow values in Eqs. (2.8) through (2.10). Secondly, the PSD was essentially the same shape as Fig. 5 for the TBL, except that the diameter of the vehicle should replace the displacement thickness as a characteristic dimension and ω/U replaces k_1.

The question of convection has not been studied experimentally, but it seems logical that convection should be absent in BPF loads. If this is the case, spatial correlation experiments will still be required to determine the form of $\phi_p(\xi_1,\xi_3,0)$. In the absence of such data, one may assume a correlation form for estimation purposes. The replacement of the environment with a sound field is one example. Another possibility is to assume a relation between spatial scale and correlation that is logical and convenient, for example, the form of Eq. (2.6) with L = D, the vehicle (or base) diameter.

Base Pressure Fluctuations

Base pressure fluctuations (BPF) occur in regions of separated flow on the aft section of a vehicle as shown in Fig. 7. Pressure fluctuations in this region of the vehicle may be expected to be somewhat different from those at more forward positions on the vehicle for two reasons: (a) there is no reason to expect significant convection effects for BPF, and (b) the spatial scale is set by the overall vehicle diameter.

There are only two pieces of data on BPF that are generally available. One is the previously mentioned subsonic data taken by Eldred in a wind tunnel [34], which by showing that the frequency spectrum of BPF is similar to that of the TBL in the attached regions of flow, except that the vehicle diameter replaces the displacement thickness as the characteristic dimension, generally leads to a spectrum with much greater low-frequency content. Also, since the overall rms pressure coefficient in the base is very nearly equal to that in the region of attached flow, the low-frequency loading is very much greater on the base of the vehicle than on its sides—the opposite is true, of course, for high-frequency excitation.

The second piece of data is that inferred by Benedetti and Smith [32] from base vibration and internal microphone data on an experimental reentry vehicle.

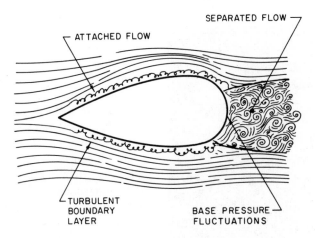

Fig. 7. Reentry vehicle aerodynamics showing regions of attached (TBL) and separated (BPF) pressure loads.

Unfortunately, the amount of data reported do not seem sufficiently conclusive to allow comparison with the subsonic data of Eldred.

Very little is known about the spatial correlation of BPF. An appealing assumption is to use the transverse spatial correlation of the TBL, replacing the displacement thickness δ^* by D, the vehicle diameter:

$$\phi \sim \exp\left(-r/D\right).$$

There is no experimental support for this, but it can be useful in estimating response of base structures and probably produces a result in the right ballpark.

2.3 Compressible Aerodynamic Loads

The most important noninertial aerodynamic load on a flight vehicle arises from the existence of shock waves. When a shock occurs, it is rarely absolutely steady, and the fluctuation in its position will cause pressure variations on the vehicle surface, generally at relatively low frequencies. The origin of the fluctuations is not clear—but they are thought to be associated with the upstream turbulent boundary layer and region of separated flow downstream. Figure 8 is a photograph of a space vehicle model in a wind tunnel that demonstrates rather clearly the incoming TBL, the shock, and the region of separated flow [35].

Measurements of fluctuating pressures in the region of an attached shock generally show augmented low-frequency pressure levels. The oscillation of the shock is one source of low-frequency loads, but the interaction of the shock with the inflowing TBL will cause acoustic pressure fluctuations, both radiated and nonradiated. Lowson has shown theoretically that quite large pressure fluctuations can be explained from this mechanism [36]. It is not clear at this time,

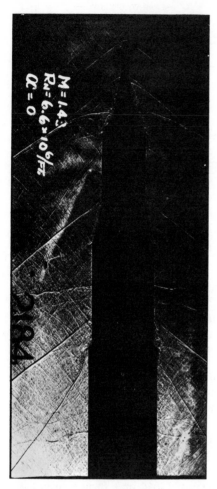

Fig. 8. Space vehicle model in supersonic flow showing shock-induced separation forward of flare [35].

however, whether or not Lowson's model can account for the apparent magnitude of the random displacement of the shock front or the observed spectrum. In any case, this part of the TBL–shock interaction must be present and will represent a contribution to the loads.

Low-frequency fluctuations will also arise from the shock-separated flow interaction. The higher pressures in the downstream side of the shock cause flow separation. The separated flow region behaves like a TBL with a very thick displacement thickness. This separated flow generates low-frequency pressures. Also, the high downstream pressure is able to penetrate the boundary layer and cause it to thicken upstream. This thickening reduces the shock strength and causes the TBL to thicken even more—resulting in the displacement of the shock to a new stable position upstream [37]. Once the shock moves to this new position, however, the downstream conditions cannot maintain it there, and it returns whence it came. And so it goes, back and forth.

This latter description seems to be drawn from analyses of certain buffeting problems [38]. It may be adequate, however, to call out the two phenomena, the shock motion and the separated flow, as significant loads. The separated flow has already been treated; here we will treat the shock motion.

Chandiramani *et al* [2] describe loads due to supersonic shock oscillation, of the kind that occur ahead of a flare in the structure, by the displacement of the shock $y(t)$ and the pressure differential across the shock Δp. The displacement is assumed to be a narrow-band process centered about frequency f_{osc} with bandwidth $f_{osc}/4$. The magnitude Δp is the pressure differential obtained from the supersonic aerodynamics of the vehicle. The rms shock displacement σ is taken to be a fraction $1/8$ of the upstream distance L from the flare to the shock. The frequency f_{osc} is obtained from

$$f_{osc} \sim 0.06 \, U/L,$$

where U is the speed of the vehicle. The spectrum of the signal that this produces in a microphone is shown in Fig. 9. Note, however, that this is not the same as the effective spectrum of generalized force on any particular mode of the structure. We shall take up the response problem in the following chapter. A summary of the estimation procedure for oscillating shock pressure spectra, their period of occurrence during the flight, and their location on the vehicle is by by Chandiramani et al. [2].

The preceding discussions give as complete a picture as possible for the current status of flight-induced fluctuating pressure environments. More details of these environments, particularly as they occur on space vehicles, can be found in Ref. 2. Nevertheless, it is clear that there are many gaps in our knowledge of flight-induced loads. It is important, however, that we not take data for its own sake, but that its intended use be considered in the experimental design.

Far too often great stress has been placed in accumulating data that have turned out to be peripheral or beside the point. A good example of this is the concern whether the correlation $\phi_1(\xi_1)$ in a TBL does or does not have a finite correlation area. Structural analysts would be wise to give their requirements to the aerodynamicists early in the loads accumulation program. In the following chapter, we have a look at response prediction models. These will indicate the loads data needed to predict response.

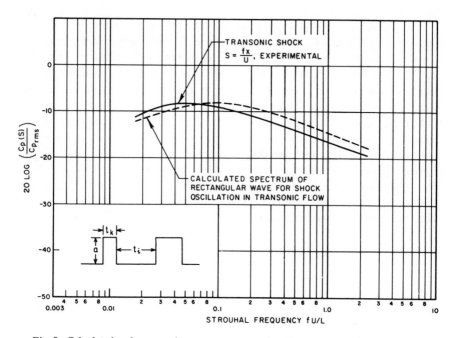

Fig. 9. Calculated and measured pressure spectra at location of an oscillating shock [2].

CHAPTER 3
ESTIMATION OF VEHICLE RESPONSE

3.1 Introduction

The design engineer and the environmental or test engineers are interested in the response of a vehicle to in-flight loads for slightly differing reasons. The test engineer is primarily concerned with the fact of vibration—*how much* vibration, *when,* and *where.* The design engineer wants the *how much* information, so that he can assess the integrity of the vehicle. But he is also concerned with the *why* of the response, since he wants to know what he can change in the event that the vibration is excessive, or to anticipate the effects of structural modifications.

The procedures for response estimation reflect this dual purpose to a degree, but it is safe to say that the test engineer has been better served. Fairly empirical estimation procedures are in common use, but there has been an effort to develop methods that relate the response more directly to structural parameters. Some of these methods still rely on empiricism for portions of the prediction procedure—we shall term these *semi-empirical.* Quite recently, some procedures have been put forward that rely much less on empiricism and much more on analysis of structural-environmental interactions. We refer to these as *rational* methods.

The goals of response estimation are (a) the providing of information on the vibration of the external structure, its frequency and spatial distribution and how these change with time; and (b) the transmission of this vibrational energy to internal structures and acoustic spaces. As the various procedures are described, the extent to which each meets these goals will be discussed.

3.2 Empirical and Semi-empirical Methods

The most direct approach to response estimation is to measure the vibration and/or sound levels experienced by a vehicle during its flight, and then to use these levels to predict the vibration of a panel, or black box, that is located on or within a similar vehicle flying a similar trajectory. Even such a straightforward procedure has difficulties that are worth mentioning.

A major difficulty derives from the method of data collection. Space vehicle systems thus far use telemetry rather than on-board recorders to gather most of the data. In many cases the vehicle is not recovered; in others the weight of a recorder is judged too great for inclusion in the payload. The frequency response of a telemetry channel is limited—a bandwidth up to a few kilohertz at the most—

and the number of channels is limited. Thus, the relayed information does not usually contain much high-frequency data.

Recorders can be carried in aircraft, and the frequency range of available data is greater than it is for spacecraft. A difficulty shared by both, however, is that due to the size of these vehicles and the many kinds of structures involved, the number of observation locations is not adequate for good determination of response or for adequate definition of the subsystem environment. Nevertheless, with repeated flights, a good library of flight data can be built up, and the vibration or internal sound levels at a great number of locations during a flight can be predicted for the vehicle.

The methodology involved in this data collection is rather straightforward. The process of converting the data into a prescribed vibration environment may be rather more involved, however. Typically, the output of a three-axis accelerometer located at some sensitive position is monitored as a function of time. This signal is analyzed in frequency bands, and the spectrum at different times is plotted. The levels are likely to be large during specific portions of the flight (launch, transonic, or max Q). The spectra for these portions of the flight are then converted into test power spectral densities, usually prescribed by the slope and magnitude of the spectrum over frequency intervals. It is in the conversion of the environmental data to test spectra that most of the vagaries arise.

A typical example of reduced vibration data is shown in Fig. 10. Such a spectrum is too complicated to prescribe as a test spectrum, and in addition, it is only a typical one—other flights and other locations will produce similar, but slightly differing spectra (variations in band levels of the order of 10 dB are common). The simplest procedure is to *envelope* this spectrum with a spectrum that can be specified. Curve A in Fig. 10 is an example. In most cases this spectrum will produce a conservative test; i.e., the test is more severe than the environment. As an alternative, curve A may be lowered until the overall acceleration level of the test is the same as that of the environment, and the new test spectrum is curve B. In this case, some of the peaks in the realized environmental spectrum will exceed the test spectrum, and the engineer may be concerned that a resonance in the tested item at such frequencies may be underexposed.

In addition to these problems, the adequacy of the environmental data may be in question. If several flights are available, a composite of the data in Fig. 10 can be drawn which exceeds 80, 90, or 100 percent of the data. This in turn can be converted to a test spectrum by an enveloping procedure.

The decision process by which one converts environmental data to a test spectrum is referred to as *test philosophy*. To the cynic, uninitiated into the rites of such activities, a more appropriate word might be *theology*. In many cases, the exact procedure is unimportant—the item is developed and tested for levels above its environment. As we shall see in the following chapter, however, this is far from being the only set of vagaries in the system. Despite its importance, the problem of setting test levels has received rather little research effort. It could well benefit from some basic studies of the effect of fine-grained spectral variations on structural or component response.

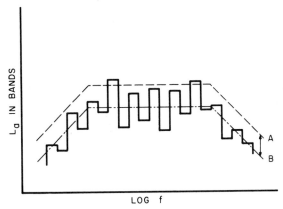

Fig. 10. Narrow-band vibration spectrum
and derived (smooth) test specifications.

The Method of Mahaffey and Smith

The trajectory (or mission) profile of a flight vehicle tends to be controlled by its design and configuration. Some variations will be encountered. The trajectory of a launch vehicle will depend on whether the flight is suborbital, orbital, or interplanetary. An aircraft has a different trajectory in landing, takeoff, reconnaissance, or attack [39].

In addition to trajectory variations, the vehicle itself may have structural changes. Its engines may be relocated, it may be shortened, or certain sections may have smaller geometrical changes. To capitalize on information previously gathered on the vehicle, several methods have been devised to allow one to translate the old data to new circumstances. One of these is the so-called Mahaffey-Smith (M-S) method. We will illustrate this method by employing the same example used by Mahaffey and Smith.

The initial step is a fairly complete sound and vibration survey—in this instance a measurement of acceleration and sound pressures analyzed in octave bands at various locations on the B-58 airplane shown in Fig. 11. The authors expressed the response as *peak* acceleration, which is three times the rms value the response; defining the peak as that level that is crossed 1 percent of the time (which is consistent with the response being Gaussian). In Fig. 12, we have reproduced a set of the data for the 600 to 1200 Hz octave band, using the rms as a measure of the acceleration.

The data generally appear to fit a linear regression line rather well in all the octave bands studied. Assuming a log-normal distribution for the rms accelerations for a given sound pressure level L_p (vibration data in complex structures seem to fit this distribution surprisingly well in a wide variety of circumstances), the variance of the measured data is noted and confidence levels for each band are also drawn, as shown. In general, the form of the regression line is

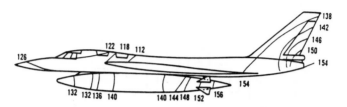

Fig. 11. Contours of constant L_p on B-58 airplane for 600 to 1200 Hz octave band [40].

$$L_a = ML_p + A, \qquad (3.1)$$

where A is a measure of the *acceptance* of the structure and M is the slope. Both M and A vary from one frequency band to the next, but the range of M is from 0.5 at the lower bands to 0.7 in the upper bands.

The observation that $M \neq 1$ has led some observers to suspect nonlinear behavior of the structure. There are other more likely reasons for a lack of proportionality between pressure and acceleration, however. One of these is the tendency of vibrational energy to propagate through the structure from a region of high excitation to a region of low excitation. Thus, regions of high excitation have less response than if they were not connected to other structure, while regions of lower excitation have more. Whether mechanical transmission can account for the behavior of the field data has not been determined at present.

Finally, one derives vibration estimates from the set of curves such as those in Fig. 12 by measuring the sound pressure levels L_p on a section of the vehicle not previously measured. The values of L_p for each frequency band are plotted, and the curves like Fig. 12 are consulted. The appropriate confidence coefficient is then chosen, and the corresponding acceleration level in each band is read. This set of levels vs frequency becomes the response estimate, and may be used as is, or averaged (smoothed) in some way to serve as an environmental specification.

It is relatively easy to find fault with the M-S procedure. It ignores structural differences throughout the vehicle, it is not specific as to how measurements are to be taken, and it is devoid of structural or geometric scaling parameters. For these reasons, and others, it has on occasion been misused. It is more instructive, however, to inquire why it has received so much attention. There are at least three reasons why this is so. First, the M-S procedure is relatively simple to carry out. It requires the existence of a similar operational vehicle, and the taking of a fair amount of sound and vibration data to obtain the basic information. The gathering of this information is straightforward, however. Second, it generates an estimate that is easy to interpret. Finally, the estimate of response is in the proper form for application.

Franken Estimate for Cylindrical Vehicles

The M-S procedure does not take into account the effect of any structural differences on the response at two different portions of the vehicle exposed to the same fluctuating pressure levels. Franken has pointed out that if one examines the response of cylindrical vehicles to acoustic excitation, then the ratio of rms acceleration to rms pressure reaches a maximum near the *ring frequency* f_r for the vehicle, and has a rapid falloff above f_r [41]. The ring frequency is that frequency for which the longitudinal wavelength in the skin material is equal to the vehicle circumference $2\pi a$:

$$f_r = c_\ell/2\pi a. \tag{3.2}$$

The second observation is that the response appears to be well normalized to the limp wall response of the vehicle, the response that the pressures would induce into a structure of the same surface mass density but having no rigidity. For such a vehicle, the ratio of acceleration to pressure is constant

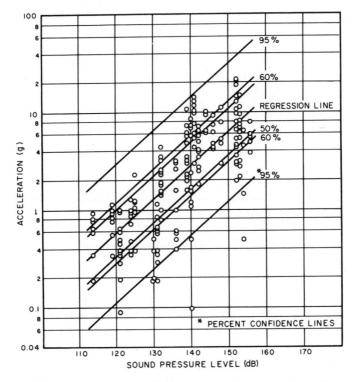

Fig. 12. Scatter diagram of acceleration levels L_a on B-58 airplane plotted against pressure levels L_p in 600 to 1200 Hz octave band [40].

a = Acceleration
p = Pressure
W = Surface density

$$W^2 a^2 / p^2 = 1. \tag{3.3}$$

Using a pressure reference of 0.0002 dyne/sq cm, the acceleration of gravity as a reference for acceleration level, and expressing the surface density of the panel W in pounds per square foot, one gets the mass law response formula

$$L_{a(ML)} + 20 \log W - L_p = -128. \tag{3.4}$$

The mass law acceleration is plotted in Fig. 13 along with the cross-hatched band representing the distribution of observed response on Jupiter and Titan I vehicles as analyzed by Franken. We see that the actual response increases from the mass law base line to approximately 8 dB above mass law at the ring frequency and drops off to mass law levels at a few octaves above f_r.

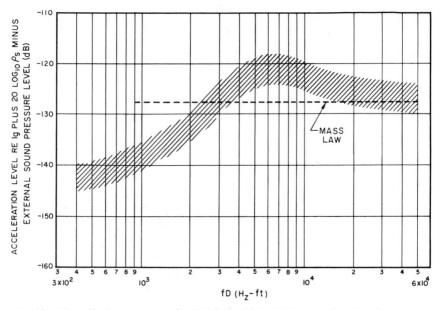

Fig. 13. Normalized acceptance of cylindrical vehicles of diameter D and surface weight W [41].

We have termed Franken's method semi-empirical because it does use notions of structural detail such as ring frequency and surface density. It nevertheless is empirical in that it relies exclusively on data for the establishment of an estimate. It is not clear at this point whether it is consistent with the M-S method. It may be, since in an aircraft, regions of high excitation tend to have smaller diameter (see Fig. 11) and the change in f_r and surface density as one proceeds along the fuselage may combine to give results such as those in Fig. 12. The available data from the M-S paper do not permit this comparison.

Franken's procedure has been very useful for estimating skin vibration for cylindrical vehicles. It may be possible to develop extensions of it to predict the transmission of sound and vibration to interior compartments and structures.

Response Estimation Procedure of Eldred

The fact that Franken's empirical estimate is 8 dB or so above mass law response indicates that it is the resonant, damping limited response of the structure that is dominant near the ring frequency. In a series of reports and papers, Eldred and his colleagues have attempted to use this observation to inject additional structural information into the estimation of response [42]. They have done this by developing an analogy to the response of a simple resonator.

Consider a resonator with a resonance frequency f_o, mass M and damping loss factor η where $\eta \ll 1$. Suppose the random force applied to the resonator has a rather smooth frequency spectrum $S(f)$. The mean square acceleration of the resonator is given by [43]

$$\langle a^2 \rangle = \frac{\pi}{2} \frac{S(f_o) \cdot f_o}{\eta M^2}. \tag{3.5}$$

In analogy with this, the skin acceleration of a structure of area A and surface density W is assumed to be of the form

$$\langle a^2 \rangle = \frac{\pi}{2} \beta^2 \frac{S_p(f) f}{\eta W^2}, \tag{3.6}$$

where $S_p(f)$ is the spectral density of the pressure fluctuations. The parameter β is a measure of how well the pressure field is able to excite the mode(s) that resonate in the frequency band under consideration.

In the later discussion of statistical energy analysis, we can place an analytical interpretation on β. In Eldred's approach, however, the emphasis is on the empirical determination of β through the analysis of missile vibration data. The efficiency of structural excitation depends on the ratio of the acoustic to structural wavelength. If a structure has all dimensions scaled by a constant factor K, then, assuming similarity in the excitation, the motion of the original structure at frequency f is geometrically preserved in the model at frequency f/K. Since the acoustic field will preserve its similarity in scale K at frequency f/K, we can expect that the factor β will be unchanged. Since the radius of the vehicle a can be taken as a measure of its size, Eldred suggested that β be considered a function of $ka = 2\pi a/\lambda_a$, where λ_a is the acoustic wavelength.

Since $fS_p(f)$ is proportional to the mean square pressure in constant percentage bandwidths, Eq. (3.6) would suggest that the ratio $fS_p(f)/\langle a^2 \rangle$ should depend only on ka. In Fig. 14, we show the values of β as determined by Eldred from rocket vehicle vibration data. The data show a spread of approximately 12 dB and a general drop-off of 5 dB/decade with ka. The data are generally distributed about $\beta \sim 1$, which is the *simple resonator* value.

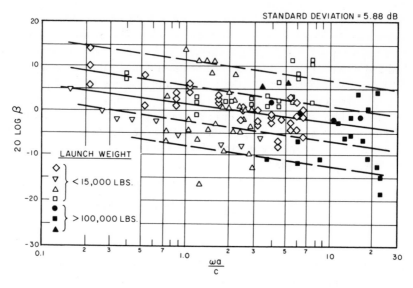

Fig. 14. Experimentally derived values of factor β for various rocket vehicles [42].

It would be interesting to compare the data of Eldred and Franken by reducing both to the same form. Unfortunately, this is made more difficult by the presumption of a single resonance in Eldred's approach. The original measurement bandwidth has been factored out of Eldred's data, so that the original band pressure level corresponding to the measured value of $\langle a^2 \rangle$ cannot be determined. One comparison can be made, however. Most of Franken's data shows a maximum in acceptance or response at $2\pi a/\lambda_\ell \simeq 1$, where λ_ℓ is the longitudinal wavelength in the structural material. This corresponds to $ka = \lambda_\ell/\lambda_a \simeq 15$ for aluminum or steel structures in air. Eldred's data do not particularly indicate any maximum or break in slope at this value of ka. We shall want to examine implications of the methods of both Franken and Eldred further in the subsequent discussions of rational procedures for response estimation.

3.3 Rational Approaches to Response Estimation

What we have termed rational approaches to response estimation are methods of computation based on the dynamic equations of motion of the structure.

This does not mean, of course, that empirical methods of the previous section are to be regarded as irrational. We also note that considerable empiricism may be involved in rational procedures in the choice of structural models, selection of parameters, and assumptions regarding the loading by the environment.

The general problem is, of course, the excitation of continuous structures by loads that are random in time and are either spatially coherent (oscillating shock) or incoherent (TBL, BPF, or sound). The most direct approach is to assume a very ideal structure, for which the modes of vibration are well known, and let it be excited by a noise field of known coherence properties. This was the approach taken by Lyon for strings [44, 45], by Powell for membranes [46], and by Dyer for plates [47]. In addition, Ribner has studied infinite plate response [48] and Cottis derived results for the modes of a cylinder [49].

As helpful as much of this work was, it was recognized that actual structures were more complex in their behavior than the simple models that had been treated. Several attempts to treat more complex systems have been made. They include studies of multiple panel bays and panels and beams with finite terminating impedances [50-53].

Finally, there have been analytical studies that have attempted to derive theoretical results in a form directly comparable to the empirical methods. In this approach, known generally as statistical energy analysis, the desire is to predict average response in frequency bands. These same techniques have also been applied to the transmission of vibrational and acoustic energy to regions within a vehicle [54].

Vibration Estimation in Simple Structures

The earliest studies of the random excitation of continuous structures by noise fields were concerned with Brownian motion of strings, beams, etc., when immersed in a fluid at temperature T. The forcing function from the fluid is generally taken to be purely random in space and time, with a correlation

$$\langle p(x,t)\, p(x',t') \rangle = D\, \delta(x - x')\, \delta(t - t'). \tag{3.7}$$

The parameter D is fixed by requiring that the energy of vibration reach a value of $1/2\, kT$ for each structural degree of freedom [55].

There are some interesting engineering problems for which the loading correlation is similar to that in Eq. (3.7). A popular model for some processes is *rain on the roof*, short period impulses occurring randomly in time and space. The turbulent boundary layer, when convected slowly, may be modeled by such a process.

To demonstrate the calculation procedure, let us imagine that the equation of motion of the responding system may be written in the form

$$\left(\frac{\partial^2}{\partial t^2} + \beta\, \frac{\partial}{\partial t} \right) w + Lw = p/\rho, \tag{3.8}$$

where L is a linear operator on the displacement w and represents the elastic restoring forces in the system. The damping is introduced through the viscous coefficient β, and the appropriate mass density is ρ. While this is not the most general system one can postulate, it is sufficient for a discussion of most methods developed to date.

If the boundary conditions are specified, then the eigenfunctions (natural modes) of the operator L are determined from

$$L\psi_M = \omega_M^2 \psi_M, \tag{3.9}$$

with the normalization condition

$$\langle \psi_M \psi_N \rangle_s = \delta_{MN}, \tag{3.10}$$

where δ_{MN} is the Kronecker delta, and the average is spatial average over the surface of the structure.

If the displacement w and the pressure p are expanded in a series of the modal shape functions,

$$\left. \begin{aligned} p(x,t) &= \sum \psi_M(x)\, P_M(t) \\ w(x,t) &= \sum \psi_M(x)\, W_M(t) \end{aligned} \right\}, \tag{3.11}$$

then Eq. (3.8) becomes

$$\frac{d^2 W_M}{dt^2} + \beta\, \frac{dW_M}{dt} + \omega_M^2 W_M = \rho^{-1} P_M, \tag{3.12}$$

where

$$\left. \begin{aligned} P_M(t) &= \langle p(x,t)\, \psi_M(x) \rangle_s \\ W_M(t) &= \langle w(x,t)\, \psi_M(x) \rangle_s \end{aligned} \right\}. \tag{3.13}$$

There are several ways to obtain a solution of Eq. (3.12), but a popular one is to use the impulse function [56]:

$$h_M(t) = \frac{1}{\omega_M'}\, e^{-\beta t/2}\, \sin \omega_M' t, \tag{3.14}$$

where

$$\omega_M' = (\omega_M^2 - \beta^2/4)^{1/2}.$$

If the damping is small, $\omega_M \simeq \omega_M'$.

In terms of the impulse response,

$$W_M(t) = \rho^{-1} \int_{-\infty}^{t} dt'' \, h_M(t - t'') P_M(t''). \tag{3.15}$$

The modal amplitude $W_M(t)$ is of little value in itself, since $P_M(t')$ and hence $W_M(t)$ are random functions of time and are only specified by their statistics. The *crosscorrelation* of the modal amplitudes can be written

$$\langle W_M(t) W_N(t') \rangle = \rho^{-2} \int_{-\infty}^{t} dt'' \int_{-\infty}^{t'} dt''' h_M(t - t'') h_N(t - t''') \langle P_M(t'') P_N(t''') \rangle_{ens}, \tag{3.16}$$

where the notation $\langle \ldots \rangle_{ens}$ means *ensemble average of* as distinct from the spatial averages defined previously. By using Eq. (3.13), the *source term* in Eq. (3.16) is

$$\langle P_M(t'') P_N(t''') \rangle = \langle\langle \psi_M(x) \psi_N(x') \langle p(x,t'') p(x',t''') \rangle_{ens} \rangle_s \rangle_s, \tag{3.17}$$

where

$$\langle p(x,t'') p(x',t''') \rangle_{ens} = \langle p^2 \rangle \, \phi_p(x - x', t'' - t''') \tag{3.18}$$

is the space-time pressure correlation field. We have discussed the form of this function for TBL's and regions of separated flow in the preceding chapter.

Using the preceding formulation and the model of the pressure field correlation of turbulent flow,

$$\phi_p(x,t) = A_t \, \delta(x - U_c t) e^{-t/\theta}, \tag{3.19}$$

Lyon [44] calculated the response of a ribbon to a turbulent pressure field convected along its length. In a similar set of calculations, Dyer [47] computed the response of a rectangular supported plate to a similar convected and decaying correlation field.

These calculations showed several interesting features of the response of structural modes to a convected TBL: (a) if the convection speed is very low, the excitation is similar to rain on the roof; and (b) there is augmented response for modes that are resonant and have a trace wave speed in the direction of convection that equals the convection speed. For a given frequency this can occur only when the convection speed exceeds the speed of flexural waves on the structure. The modal amplitude as a function of convection speed is shown in Fig. 15. As we shall see, these are the important forms of response behavior for structures that are more complex than simple strings or plates.

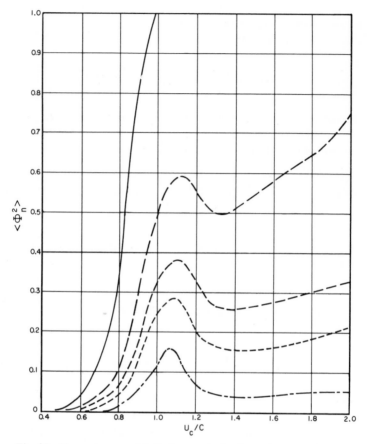

Fig. 15. Mean square modal displacement of string as function of convection velocity [45].

Let us now assume that the excitation is confined to a single frequency ω. We use the complex convection $e^{-i\omega t}$. Then

$$P_M(t) = P_M e^{-i\omega t} \left.\right\}$$
$$W_M(t) = W_M e^{-i\omega t} \left.\right\}, \qquad (3.20)$$

where P_M and W_M are complex amplitude factors. Placing these in Eq. (3.12),

$$W_M = \frac{-P_M/\rho}{\omega^2(1 + i\beta) - \omega_M^2}. \qquad (3.21)$$

The mean square displacement in time is

$$\langle w^2(x,t)\rangle_t = \frac{1}{2} Re \sum_{M,N} \psi_M(x)\psi_N(x) \frac{P_M P_N^* / \rho^2}{\{\omega^2(1+i\beta) - \omega_M^2\}\{\omega^2(1+i\beta) - \omega_N^2\}}.$$

(3.22)

We can generalize the result of Eq. (3.16) by considering the Fourier transform of the pressure:

$$p(x,\omega) = \lim_{T\to\infty} \int_{-T}^{T} p(x,t)e^{i\omega t}\, dt.$$

(3.23)

If the correlation in Eq. (3.18) depends only on the time difference, then it may also be written

$$\langle p(x',t)p(x'',t')\rangle_t = \frac{1}{2\pi}\int_{-\infty}^{\infty} d\omega\, P(x',x'';\omega)e^{-i\omega t},$$

(3.24)

where

$$P(x',x'';\omega) = \lim_{T\to\infty} (2T)^{-1}\langle p(x,\omega)p^*(x'',\omega)\rangle_{ens}$$

(3.25)

is called the cross-power spectral density. If we place Eq. (3.28) into Eq. (3.13), and substitute into Eq. (3.22), we get

$$\langle w^2(x,t)\rangle = \frac{1}{2\rho^2} Re \sum_{M,N} \psi_M(x)\psi_N(x) \int_{-\infty}^{\infty} d\omega \frac{\langle P(x',x'';\omega)\psi_M(x')\psi_N(x'')\rangle}{Y_M Y_N^*}$$

$$= \frac{\langle p^2\rangle}{2\rho^2} \sum_{M,N} \psi_M(x)\psi_N(x) \int_{-\infty}^{\infty} \frac{j_{MN}^2(\omega)\, d\omega}{|Y_M Y_N^*|},$$

(3.26)

where

$$Y_M = \omega^2(1+i\beta) - \omega_M^2$$

and

$$j_{MN}^2(\omega) \equiv \langle p^2\rangle^{-1}\langle P(x',x'';\omega)\psi_M(x')\psi_N(x'')\rangle_{s',s''}$$

(3.27)

is called the *joint acceptance* of the modes M,N. This function was originally introduced by Powell [46].

The result (Eq. 3.26) has been widely applied by design engineers because it is assumed that the mode shapes, the modal admittances, and the joint acceptances are readily computed or measured. However, particularly at higher frequencies, the excitation of response may be dominated by rather subtle alterations in the mode shapes or the spatial coherence of the excitation.

The joint acceptance method has been applied by Powell to strings [57] and by his associates to membranes, panels, and other structures. In some of his papers, Powell also suggested how his methods might be extended in an approximate fashion to apply to more complex vibrational systems at higher frequencies [58]. We shall return to this topic below.

Applications to Complex Structures

When one tries to apply the formalism of Eqs. (3.16) or (3.26) to a more complex structure such as a flight vehicle, then the situation naturally becomes much more complex. The definition of the crosscorrelation (or cross-power spectrum) over an extended surface is tedious, and the mode shapes for realistic structural segments may not be known. The determination of exact resonance frequencies and values of modal loss factors are also difficult, although their average properties can be estimated.

Most effort in the direct extension of the basic formulation has been centered on analyzing the modal patterns of the structure. The multiply supported panel has been analyzed by P. W. Smith, Jr. [52], by Y. K. Lin at University of Illinois [50, 51], and by Colin Mercer at Southampton [53]. The motivation, of course, is the similarity between the multiply supported panel and the multiple bay panels on aircraft and other structures. It is found that there is a theoretical difference between the behavior of N disconnected panels and N connected panels, but the analyses and experiments have not been able to demonstrate that the rather idealized connected panels are more representative of flight structures than are the simpler unconnected panels.

In many ways, the large, modern, high-speed digital computer seems to offer a panacea for the problem of structural complexity. The computer can be quite helpful in calculating the lower order modes of rather complicated structures consisting of combinations of stringers, ring frames, reinforced cutouts, etc. The mode shapes and resonance frequencies are obtained directly in the output. The required input is generally the damping, the exciting forces, and considerable structural detail. The amount of time required to program, perform, and process the calculations depends in a fairly direct way on the number of calculations involved. This can easily be estimated by considering how fine-grained the computation must be in frequency and space for adequate accuracy.

Consider a 1/8-in. thick aluminum shroud, 6 ft in diameter and 15 ft long. Suppose that we are interested in its vibratory response from 100 to 2500 Hz (a typical range of interest). The finest linear spatial scale is about one-quarter of a bending wavelength at the highest frequency of interest. In our example, the wavelength is 4 in. The number of mesh-points is approximately 4×10^4. If only a single component of vibration (i.e., transverse) is important then this represents the number of simultaneous equations to be solved at each frequency.

To obtain a good statistic in the frequency domain, we require at least one calculation every modal bandwidth. For the example, if we choose a loss factor of 0.01, then at 1000 Hz, the bandwidth is 10 Hz and we would require (at least) 240 repetitions of the calculations for reasonable spectral definition.

The reader may object that there are interesting problems to be solved where the number of required mesh points and frequencies is not so great. This is true. In the case of sound and vibration transmission, however, we must include the descriptions of acoustic media and connecting structures. In addition, we frequently want to know response sensitivity to changes in parameters such as damping, skin thickness, and frame spacing. Even in modest systems, the number of degrees of freedom increases rapidly as we include the frequencies of direct engineering interest.

Because of the above considerations and others such as cost, time, and output format, digital computer calculations using finite element models have been of quite marginal value in analyzing sound and vibration response of structures. There is considerable literature on the subject, and we feel that including it here would dilute the material that we regard as more significant to our present purposes.

Beginning in the early 1960's, a new approach to the excitation of complex structures by random environments began to appear. These studies, known collectively as *statistical energy analysis* (SEA) have been centered mostly at Bolt Beranek and Newman, but other groups have also made contributions to the literature in this area. Broadly speaking, an attempt is made to model the structural system by an assemblage of modes whose primary parameters (resonance frequency, damping, mode shape, etc.) are statistically determined. The primary dynamic variable is chosen to be the energy of vibration, from which other variables (acceleration, strain, etc.) may be determined. Much of the *inspiration* for this point of view has been derived from the methods of the statistical analysis of room acoustics.

Statistical modeling and the use of energy variables would likely be valuable additions to the tool kit of the analyst in themselves, but two other principles increase the power of SEA appreciably. It has been shown that parameter statistics calculated for quite simple systems may be applied to more complex systems. For example, the average modal density (number of modal resonances occurring in a frequency interval) may be computed for the flexural resonances of a simple rectangular supported panel, but the result of this calculation is applicable to any panel of the same area, when one considers resonance frequencies well above the fundamental.

The second principle states that under random excitation, the flow of mechanical power from one system mode to another is proportional to the difference in their time average energies. This principle allows one to infer the direction and magnitude of energy flow in a system, once the input power and dissipative processes are determined. Such calculations are necessary when considering the transmission of sound and vibration in flight vehicles.

It would be very difficult to review all the applications that have been made of SEA. Rather than do this, we shall summarize briefly many of these calculations and experiments in the following few paragraphs. Subsequent to this, we shall review in rather more detail its application to a spacecraft-shroud combination excited by a sound field.

Review of SEA Applications

The earliest studies that applied the ideas of modal density and asymptotic behavior of mechanical systems to structural response must include those of Powell [58] and Skudrzyk [59] in 1958. Powell showed that certain response averages over modes were equivalent to the same averages over infinite structures. In his analysis, Skudrzyk examined the input impedance of multimodal structures and showed that the modal density has a central role in the bridge between asymptotic modal behavior and behavior of the same system infinitely extended.

The response of *infinite* plates and cylinders to a TBL pressure field were carried out by Corcos and Liepmann [60] and by Ribner [48]. Dyer, however, appears to be the first to group resonant modal response into frequency bands, and develop response spectra for finite systems. He used the calculations of modal response to TBL pressures, and the modal density of a flat plate to predict the displacement spectrum. The result that Dyer obtained is fully equivalent to the infinite system results of Corcos and Liepmann.

The panel response to a TBL pressure field is simplified if one does not consider the reaction of the fluid to panel vibration (except in average ways represented by mass loading and radiation damping). The response of a panel to sound is very much related to its ability to radiate sound. Smith has shown that reciprocity arguments can be applied to acoustically induced panel response calculations [61]. Since the energy exchange between the sound field and the structure is conservative, and both have energy storage capabilities, the need for a principle of energy sharing between randomly excited systems is evident.

The simplest system for the study of energy sharing between mechanical systems is a pair of simple resonators. The power flow between two randomly excited resonators with weak, linear coupling was studied by Lyon and Maidanik [62]. The result showed that the power flow was proportional to the difference in time average energy of the resonators and that it flows from the resonator of higher energy to the one of lower energy. More recently, Scharton [63] and Ungar [64] have shown that the weak coupling restriction can be removed, and Newland [65] has extended the result to include certain forms of nonlinear coupling elements.

The two-resonator system is of relatively little interest in itself. One is usually concerned about sets of resonators (modes) that may exchange energy. If one can argue (or demonstrate) that the energies of the modes in a particular group are nearly equal, then the interactions of that modal group with other mode sets can be calculated using the single resonator pair results. This approach is taken by Lyon [66], Maidanik [67], and Manning and Maidanik [68] in studying the interaction of an elastic panel with sound. The energy interaction between two elastic structures has been studied by Lyon and Eichler [69] and by Scharton [63]. A recent survey of the relation between multimodal and mode-pair energy sharing has been prepared by Ungar [64].

Finally, there is a set of problems concerning the transmission of energy through a system by one or more paths. The system that we shall discuss in some detail below is of this type. Studies of sound transmission through structures using SEA have been made by Lyon [70], Eichler [71] and White [72]. A study of vibration transmission in a 3-element structure has been carried out by Lyon and Scharton [73]. A study of sound *and* vibration transmission in a spacecraft system has been completed recently by Manning, Lyon and Scharton [7]. This is the example that we shall treat below.

In summary, the SEA treats energy distributions in multi-element systems by (a) computing mechanical power injected into the elements by the environment, and (b) by calculating the redistribution of this energy throughout the system due to dissipative processes and to inter-element coupling. It is still a set of procedures under development, but its results to date suggest that it has an important role to play in prediction of response to environmental loads.

Example of Spacecraft Vibration Prediction

The vibration of a spacecraft at launch is primarily due to the acoustic noise exterior to the vehicle. Let us consider the spacecraft shown in Fig. 16 as an example. Since a sound field stores mechanical energy, we call this element 1. The energy of the sound field is converted into vibrational energy by the exterior structure or *shroud* of the spacecraft. This is element 2. The exterior structure in turn radiates acoustic energy into the air space contained within the structure. This air space is element 3. Finally, the structural panels of the spacecraft, element 4, are excited by this sound field into vibration.

Figure 16 shows an additional path of energy transmission. This path includes the ring frame, element 5, the mounting trusses, element 6, and the spacecraft. We shall want to include these elements as a path for mechanical energy in parallel to the acoustic path. These paths are shown diagramatically in Fig. 17.

Consider the acoustic path first. We imagine the exterior sound field to be contained in a large room of volume V. If the space-time rms pressure in this field in a band of width Δ is p_1, then the average energy of an acoustic mode is

$$\frac{E_1}{n_1 \Delta} = \frac{p^2}{\rho c^2} V \frac{1}{n_1 \Delta}. \qquad (3.28)$$

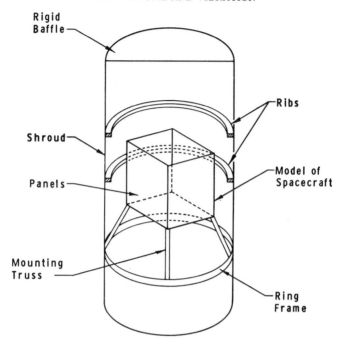

Fig. 16. Sketch of spacecraft-shroud assembly used in analysis of sound and vibration transmission [7].

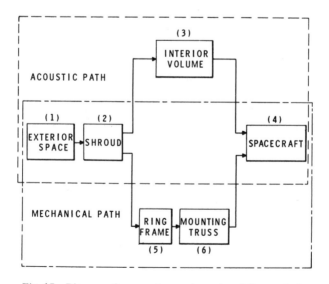

Fig. 17. Diagram of energy storage elements and flow paths in spacecraft-shroud system [7].

The first factor is the acoustic energy density and n_1 is the number of acoustic modes per unit frequency bandwidth. This quantity is termed the modal density and is given by

$$n_1(f) = 4\pi^2 f^2 V/c^3. \tag{3.29}$$

Note that the volume V cancels out of Eq. (3.29).

The energy balance equation for the shroud must include the power supplied to it by the sound field, the power that it radiates to the interior space, and the power that it dissipates internally. Formally

$$\Pi_{1,2} = \Pi_{2,3} + \Pi_2^{diss}, \tag{3.30}$$

or, introducing dissipative and coupling loss-factors,

$$\eta_{1,2} n_1 \left[\frac{E_1}{n_1} - \frac{E_2}{n_2} \right] = \eta_{2,3} \left[\frac{E_2}{n_2} - \frac{E_3}{n_3} \right] + \eta_2 E_2. \tag{3.31}$$

The left side of this equation shows the proportionality of power flow from 1 to 2 on the difference in modal energies of sound field and shroud. The first term on the right is the power flow from the shroud to the interior space, while the final term represents the dissipation in the shroud. The quantities $\eta_{1,2}$ and $\eta_{2,3}$ are the "coupling loss factors," and they must be calculated or measured for the system. The dissipation loss factor η_2 is usually obtained experimentally.

If the transmission of sound to element 3 is temporarily ignored, then $\eta_{2,3} \to 0$ in Eq. (3.31) and the ratio E_2/E_1 can be obtained from Eq. (3.31). The modal density n_2 is derived from shell dynamics of cylinders [74, 75] and $\eta_{1,2}$ is obtained by using a consistency relationship.

The left-hand side of Eq. (3.31) represents the power flow from element 1 to element 2. If we were writing an energy balance for element 1, we would include this same term in the form

$$-\eta_{2,1} n_2 \left(\frac{E_2}{n_2} - \frac{E_1}{n_1} \right),$$

since it represents energy lost from element 1. But these power flows are equal. We therefore have the consistency relationship

$$n_1 \eta_{1,2} = n_2 \eta_{2,1}. \tag{3.32}$$

The importance of this is that the modal densities are relatively easy to calculate, and if we know one of the coupling loss factors, we do not have to compute the other. In this particular instance, $\eta_{2,1}$ is known since it is very simply related to the radiation resistance of a cylindrical shell [67]:

$$\eta_{2,1} = \frac{R_{rad}}{\omega M_2}. \tag{3.33}$$

The modal density n_2 and coupling loss factor are shown in Figs. 18 and 19 for a glass fiber shroud 195 in. long, 65 in. in diameter and 0.13 in. thick. Note the peak in both the modal density and the coupling loss factor at the ring frequency. The energy E_2 is related to the space-time mean square transverse acceleration of the cylinder by

$$E_2 = M_2 \langle a_2^2 \rangle / \omega^2. \tag{3.34}$$

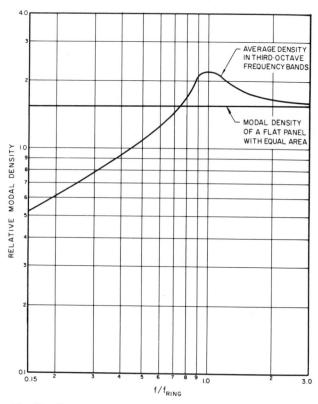

Fig. 18. Modal density of cylinder, averaged in one-third octave bands, compared to flat plate of equal area [7].

If in addition, we assume loss factors of $\eta_2 = 10^{-2}$ and 3.16×10^{-2} for the shroud, then the predicted acoustically induced response is shown in Fig. 20. It is interesting to compare this calculated response with the semi-empirical prediction of Franken in Fig. 13.

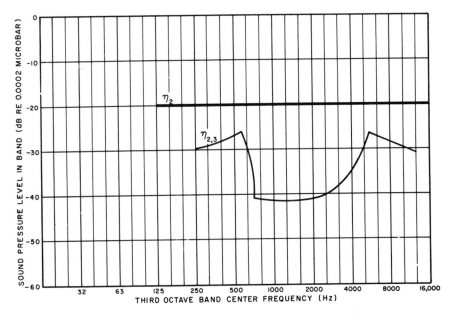

Fig. 19. Shroud-sound field coupling loss factor and dissipative loss factor of shroud [7].

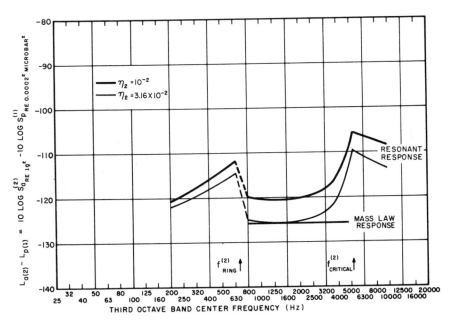

Fig. 20. Acoustic acceptance of shroud for two values of structural damping [7].

The energy equations for the interior acoustic space are similar to Eq. (3.30):

$$\Pi_{2,3} + \Pi_{1,3}^{NR} = \Pi_{3,4} + \Pi_3^{diss} \qquad (3.35)$$

or, again introducing the loss factors,

$$\omega n_2 \eta_{2,3}\left(\frac{E_2}{n_2} - \frac{E_3}{n_3}\right) + \Pi_{1,3}^{NR} = \omega n_3 \eta_{3,4}\left(\frac{E_3}{n_3} - \frac{E_4}{n_4}\right) + \eta_3 E_3. \qquad (3.36)$$

In this equation, an additional term has been added to account for power flow directly from the external sound field to the enclosed space due to the vibration of shroud modes that resonate outside the frequency band Δ. In ordinary acoustics, this is the *mass law* contribution to sound transmission [76]. Since this power flow is again proportional to the differences in modal energies of systems 1 and 3,

$$\Pi_{1,3}^{NR} = \omega \eta_{1,3} n_1 \left(\frac{E_1}{n_1} - \frac{E_3}{n_3}\right), \qquad (3.37)$$

where the coupling loss factor $\eta_{1,3}$ is related to the acoustic transmission loss of the shroud.

Finally, the acoustically induced energy of the spacecraft E_4 is determined by its power balance relations

$$\Pi_{3,4} = \Pi_4^{diss}, \qquad (3.38)$$

or, using loss factors and energies,

$$n_3 \eta_{3,4}\left(\frac{E_3}{n_3} - \frac{E_4}{n_4}\right) = \eta_4 E_4, \qquad (3.39)$$

since all the energy supplied to the spacecraft by the sound field in element 3 must be dissipated (neglecting the connection to the truss). Relating the energy E_4 to the surface acceleration a_4 by

$$E_4 = M_4 \langle a_4^2 \rangle / \omega^2 \qquad (3.40)$$

and then by using Eqs. (3.31), (3.36) and (3.39), we can generate a ratio of acceleration a_4 to external sound pressure p_1. This ratio is shown logarithmically in Fig. 21 as *acoustic path only*.

In calculating the acoustic transmission, the mechanical path through the ring frame (5) and truss (6) were neglected. The mechanical power supplied to the spacecraft by the truss is derived from the following power balance relations:

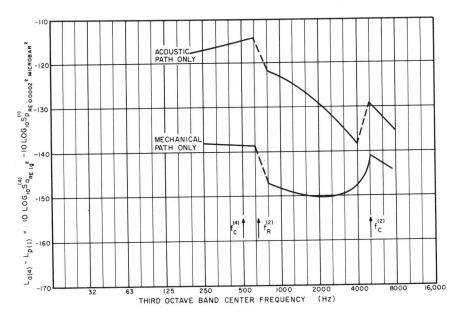

Fig. 21. Vibrational acceptance of spacecraft due to acoustic and vibrational paths separately [7].

1. For element 5, the ring frame,

$$\Pi_{2,5} = \Pi_{5,6} + \Pi_5^{diss} \qquad (3.41)$$

or

$$\eta_{2,5} n_2 \left(\frac{E_2}{n_2} - \frac{E_5}{n_5} \right) = \eta_{5,6} n_5 \left(\frac{E_5}{n_5} - \frac{E_6}{n_6} \right) + \eta_5 E_5; \qquad (3.42)$$

2. For element 6, the mounting truss,

$$\Pi_{5,6} = \Pi_{6,4} + \Pi_6^{diss} \qquad (3.43)$$

or

$$\eta_{5,6} n_5 \left(\frac{E_5}{n_5} - \frac{E_6}{n_6} \right) = \eta_{6,4} n_6 \left(\frac{E_6}{n_6} - \frac{E_4}{n_4} \right) + \eta_6 E_6; \qquad (3.44)$$

3. For element 4, the spacecraft,

$$\Pi_{6,4} = \Pi_{5,4}^{NR} = \Pi_4^{diss} \qquad (3.45)$$

or

$$\omega \eta_{6,4} n_6 \left(\frac{E_6}{n_6} - \frac{E_4}{n_4} \right) + \Pi_{5,4}^{NR} = \omega \eta_4 E_4. \qquad (3.46)$$

Again in Eq. (3.43) we have included the possibility of energy transmission from the ring frame to the spacecraft by nonresonant motion of the truss. Formally, this is given by

$$\Pi_{5,4}^{NR} = \eta_{5,4} n_5 \omega \left(\frac{E_5}{n_5} - \frac{E_4}{n_4} \right). \qquad (3.47)$$

The calculations of the coupling loss factors are carried out by Manning *et al.* [7] for the structural elements shown in Figs. 22, 23, and 24. The energy E_2 in Eq. (3.39) is assumed known by application of Fig. 15. From Eqs. (3.42), (3.44) and (3.46), one can calculate the ratio of spacecraft acceleration to external pressure p_1 due to the mechanical paths. This has been done and is plotted in Fig. 21 as *mechanical path only.*

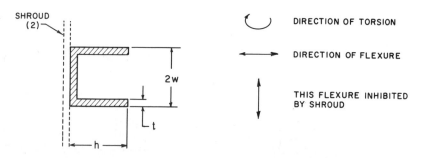

Fig. 22. Channel beam model of ring frame, element 5 [7].

In this example, the result of the calculations showed that the acoustic path was dominant, in that it produced spacecraft vibration levels of the order of 10 to 20 dB greater than did the mechanical path. We hasten to point out that this is a particular result depending on the geometry and structural parameters of the chosen configuration. Other spacecraft in a different shroud may have significantly different relative sensitivities to the acoustic and mechanical paths.

In discussing the use of SEA in this example, we have only been able to indicate the nature and order of the calculations. Much additional detail can be found in Ref. 7. It should be clear from the above, however, that while SEA offers substantial simplifications in vibration prediction over "classical" methods, it still may involve relatively lengthy computations. The length and difficulty of the

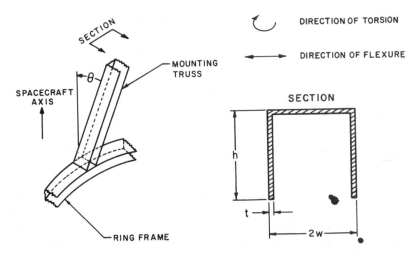

Fig. 23. Channel beam model of mounting truss, element 6 [7].

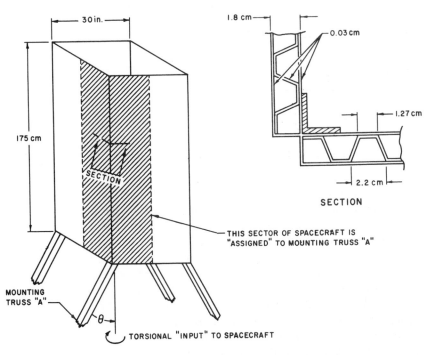

Fig. 24. Diagram of construction of spacecraft panels, element 4 [77].

calculations is usually dependent on how much cleverness and intuition one can bring to the analysis. As additional experience is gained in these studies, simplifications in the analyses will follow. It is unlikely that they will ever achieve the simplicity of the semi-empirical procedures, however, but the range of problems that SEA is able to handle is potentially much greater.

3.4 Conclusions

The prediction of vehicle response to fluctuating loads is still in a primitive state as far as the designer or test engineer is concerned. Generally, the purely empirical methods are currently used for response prediction, although some of the semi-empirical procedures may be used on existing data to scale for changes in vehicle diameter and surface mass density. The use of rational procedures, such as SEA, is still in the research stages.

An important method of determining vibratory response to loads is the use of experiments. This method simulates flight loads, and response levels are inferred by direct measurement. Since such studies are very close to the testing procedures to be discussed in the following chapter, we shall defer discussing them.

CHAPTER 4
TESTING FOR ENVIRONMENTAL EFFECTS

The role of the laboratory in environmental studies is very important. Ultimately, the best judgment of the adequacy of a design to withstand the environment must rely on laboratory acceptance or proof tests of the system and/or its components. Well-chosen simulation of the service environment will optimize the chances for a successful system, while avoiding the excessive time and costs of overdesign.

The environmental laboratory has a second role, however, that may become obscured in the pressures of system scheduling. The establishment of important structural parameters, or the determination of dominant modes of behavior as a check or substitute for theoretical derivations, is an important function for the laboratory. In this chapter, we discuss both of these functions.

4.1 Purposes of Environmental Testing

The traditional proof testing activity of the environmental laboratory is basically one of environmental simulation. The philosophy is: the equipment is to be subjected to loads that represent the most reasonably severe acoustic and/or vibration environment likely to be encountered during its mission(s). The duration of the test is set by an analysis of the time history of the load intensity, either derived from flight tests or from theoretical analysis. In some tests, such as those for fatigue of structures, the time scale of the test may be reduced by increasing the intensity of the excitation [78].

Experimental evaluation of response parameters becomes even more important when statistical energy analyses (SEA) is used as a framework for understanding structural response. As an example, the relative role of resonant and nonresonant vibration in overall response or transmission of energy can be assessed by changing the structural damping. Also, the importance of a vibration transmission path *vis a vis* an acoustic path may be determined by significantly changing the characteristics of either path; e.g., by breaking the structural connection or by adding an absorptive treatment to the acoustic spaces.

The *parameter evaluation* process just described is roughly equivalent to what has been previously described as experimental analysis [79], which is the use of experiments to ask fundamental questions about system behavior. Experimental analysis is a complement to theoretical analysis, in that it may suggest system models that are more amenable to theoretical study. This process is to be contrasted to the proof testing described earlier (which asks essentially one

47

question about the equipment—did it break?) and the *research tests* described below.

By research tests are meant experiments for determining the basic acoustic and mechanical information on a system. Such tests include the measurements of resonance frequencies and mode shapes [80], the structural damping values [81], and coupling loss factors. The results of these tests provide structural information for input to theoretical or experimental analyses. We shall not have much to say about research tests in this chapter, but guidelines for such testing are given in the references [7, Appendix].

The parameter evaluation function of the environmental laboratory is beginning to receive more attention as semi-empirical and rational methods of response estimation become more widely used. The methods of Franken [41] and Eldred [42] suggest that vehicle dimensions and weights will normalize the response to pressure ratios. Laboratory tests can readily verify whether these schemes apply to the vehicle at hand.

4.2 How Specifications Are Set

In chapter 3 we discussed how a particular vibration or acoustic spectrum measured in flight might be converted to a vibration specification. In this section, we broach a rather more complex question: how is (or should) an environmental specification be developed based on mission analysis, failure experience, and the manner of simulation. Let us review how each of these has been used for developing specifications.

The largest difference between missions is the one-shot life of space boosters, and the multi-flight lifetime of aircraft. The collection of time history data for each vehicle type is quite different. Rather complete mission profile data are collected for each spacecraft-booster combination, at least for frequency bands included in the telemetry capabilities [3]. Surprisingly, long time histories are not as available for aircraft, although steps have recently been taken to gather such data for critical sections of aircraft [82].

The type of mission profile has strong implications for the kind of failure mode that is likely to be most significant. The multi-flight mission, involving many hours of flight with intensive fluctuating pressure fields can cause metal fatigue to occur in many important structural segments. The service environment may endure so long that it is impractical to test for failure at expected levels. In these cases, the levels may be increased by a series of factors and the fatigue life recorded for each set of levels. The lifetime under service loads is then obtained by extrapolation. The shape of the excitation vs life curves is usually such that this will produce a conservative estimate of the lifetime at lower excitation levels [83].

Malfunction of single flight spacecraft has usually been identified with failure of on-board equipment. The environmental problem is more closely related to an exceedance of tolerable limits rather than a fatigue process. Accelerated, augmented amplitude testing does not make sense for this kind of failure mode. Tests of spacecraft structure and components are carried out at levels and durations that simulate the actual mission profile as closely as possible, a practicable process for the shorter duration environment of spacecraft.

The goal of the proof test is primarily a demonstration of an adequate design. Exact simulation of the loading (with a safety factor) is one way to achieve this. Exact simulation is, however, almost always beyond the state of the art and is always expensive. It is necessary, therefore, to identify the most critical part of the environment and the attendant loads. For example, in some spacecraft, the greatest vibration of electronic components may occur during lift-off, and in other spacecraft, this may occur during transonic flight. In the former, the vibration is acoustically induced, while in the latter, the excitation may be a combination of separated flow and oscillating shock.

To continue with the example, the component that fails probably does so because of mechanical strain or acceleration in its mounting and not because of the acoustic pressure surrounding it. If it sits on a circuit board, the story is different—the circuit board may be quite sensitive to the sound field, and the acoustic pressures surrounding the circuit board may be quite dependent on whether the external pressure environment is due to acoustic or separated flow [7, section 3]. Thus, simulation is seen to be a sophisticated concept. It might be adequate to simulate the vibration of the component or the loads on the spacecraft, but a simple vibration or acoustic simulation at intermediate points in the energy transmission chain may not be adequate. At this point, experimental analysis may come into play, since our evaluation studies may have shown that the circuit board was much more sensitive to the vibration of its mounting frame than to expected sound levels. We would then conclude that a vibration simulation for the board mounting was acceptable.

In the preceding paragraphs, we have assumed that the environment can be known, and simulated, if necessary, at any point in the energy transmission chain. As we discussed in chapter 2, a service noise environment is so complex that one is forced to model it with an environment achievable in the laboratory. This environment may be a reverberant sound field, or three-axis vibration excitation at a mounting point for a piece of equipment.

A separate but related problem to that of detail is the role of the dynamic interaction between systems. Thus, one may wonder if the vibration of the surface of a vehicle will produce a *break reaction* on the fluid to change acoustic or aerodynamic pressures. Theoretically, if one could produce the service pressures at the vehicle surface *under conditions of service vibration,* then the simulation would be accomplished. The same comments apply to a vibrational problem in which a mounting truss or bulkhead is mounted to a ring frame.

The difficulty in all this is reproduction of the service levels. The dynamic interaction between the two systems is embedded in the statistical covariances of the dynamic variables at the system boundaries. To reproduce the interaction effects when imposing the environment at an interface, it would be necessary to reproduce these covariances, which fluctuate rapidly as resonances of the test structure are encountered. It is usually not possible (or desirable) to attempt such a detailed simulation even if the interface data were known to such detail. For this reason, another approach to handling interaction effects is to simulate the dynamics at the interface and the environmental levels at a location away from the interface.

A simple example of this process occurs in the acoustic testing of component packages by diffuse sound fields. At very low frequencies, the acoustic wavelengths are large, and the component is merely squeezed by the sound field. At very high frequencies, the wavelengths are small compared to the dimensions of the package, and one has pressure correlations on the package that are quite similar to those in the reverberant field. In the frequency regime where wavelengths are of the order of package dimensions, however, acoustic diffraction effects can result in highly complicated spatial sound pressure correlations that are quite difficult to predict or to specify. The usual method for specifying the acoustic environment in such cases is to require that the sound field be reverberant and that its spectrum be known at a location away from the test object. The interaction effects are thus taken care of through the dynamics of the sound field-component interaction during the test.

Although not done as commonly as in acoustics, it is possible to approach the vibration interaction problem in the same way. We shall have more to say about this in section 4.3.

The definition of a specification is, therefore, a systems problem, involving the use of flight data analysis of missions, limitations and cost of facilities, possible failure modes, and desired reliability. Rarely are all these things taken into account in the environmental specification given to the equipment supplier. By the time the supplier has proof tested and delivered the item, however, most of them have had the most agonizing kind of consideration!

4.3 Direct Environmental Simulation

By *direct* environmental simulation, I mean the replacement of an acoustic environment with a sound field, or of a vibration environment by a mechanical shaker. Simulations that replace a TBL with a sound field, or a sound field with a shaker will be discussed in the following section.

Acoustic Simulation

The overall sound pressure level on flight structures may reach as much as 170 dB re 0.0002 μbar. In a progressive wave, this amounts to nearly 10^4 watts/sq ft. For a structural segment of reasonable dimensions, this means that acoustic power of the order of 10^4 to 10^6 watts is required to provide the necessary levels. It is, of course, very difficult and very expensive to generate acoustic power of this order of magnitude.

There are two large acoustic chambers in the country designed to produce sound levels of this magnitude on large vehicle segments. One of these is the Sonic Fatigue Facility [84] at Wright Field in Dayton, Ohio, shown in Fig. 25. The other is the Launch Environment Acoustic Facility [85] at the Manned Spacecraft Center in Houston, Texas. The first of these uses amplitude and frequency modulated sirens as sources, while the NASA facility uses air modulated horns. Both facilities are designed for traveling wave and reverberant field modes of operation.

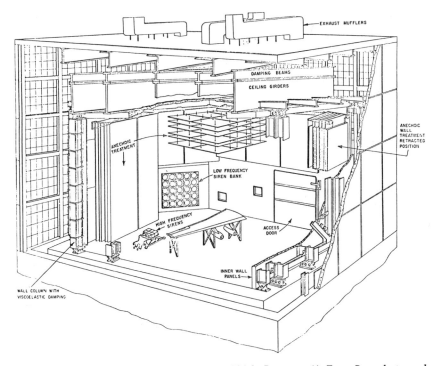

Wright-Patterson Air Force Base photograph.
Fig. 25. Sketch of Wright Field Sonic Fatigue Facility.

The production of a certain frequency spectrum of pressure over a range of positions can usually be achieved satisfactorily. Specification writers generally acknowledge that the complications of directivity of the sound cannot be achieved, so the requirements are written as *reverberant* or *traveling wave*. The spatial distribution of sound levels over the surface of the structure is also difficult to simulate in detail, but a fair latitude is usually allowed (in part because the environmental information is quite limited in this regard).

The acoustic space may have a rather subtle effect on panel dynamics. If the sound field is concentrated about the structure by close fitting duct work, then the damping and resonance frequencies of the structure may be perturbed. The increased coupling may damp the panel so strongly that the fundamental panel resonance does not appear [86].

In special circumstances, it has been desirable to test a vehicle outdoors. There are several reasons for this: (a) a semi-anechoic environment may be desired, (b) the size of the assembled vehicle may preclude chamber testing, or (c) the captive operation of other engines may provide a convenient source of high intensity sound for structural or equipment testing. Each advantage, of course, implies certain disadvantages: (a) the directional properties of the acoustic field are likely not representative of service environment, (b) the provision of handling equipment may be quite expensive, and (c) engine testing schedules may not be convenient for the structural tests. Nevertheless, such tests have proven quite useful in the past and offer an attractive and potentially inexpensive alternative to large facility construction.

Finally, we note a severe and, at present, fundamental limitation of acoustic sources—nonlinearity. As we noted above, single intense sound sources may be expected to generate power of the order of 10^3 to 10^5 watts which is carried by the sound wave. In a 1-sq ft duct, these correspond to sound pressure levels L_p from 160 to 180 dB re 0.0002 μbar. The progression of a pure tone (single frequency) wave at these levels will have the form shown in Fig. 26. In this progression, the positive peak of the wave advances until it becomes triangular after a distance [87]

$$x_c = \lambda/8M, \qquad (4.1)$$

where $M = u/c$ is the Mach number of the acoustic particle velocity and λ is the acoustic wavelength. According to Eq. (4.1), a 160 dB signal would become triangular in about 9 wavelengths. For a 500 Hz signal, this is about 18 ft.

When the wave becomes triangular, the energy that it contains is reduced by the ratio of the mean square of a triangle to a sine wave, which is 2/3 or nearly 2 dB. In addition, the 500 Hz component of the triangular wave now has its amplitude reduced by the factor $2/\pi$, representing a 4 dB loss in signal. Thus, very roughly, we can say that nonlinearity has cost us 4 dB in 500 Hz signal level. Approximately 2 dB of this is lost in frequency conversion and another 2 dB is lost in dissipative processes.

Vibration Simulation

Vibration testing is easily the most common form of environmental testing for dynamic loads. In a sense, it is a relatively simple form of testing—the vibration output of a shaker is generally uniaxial and highly controllable. It is the nearest thing that an electrical engineer will find in dynamics to the one-dimensional circuits he is accustomed to studying.

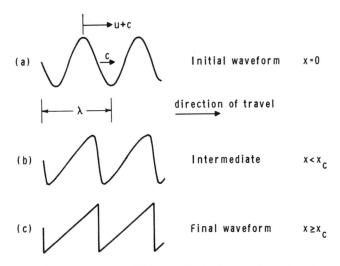

Fig. 26. Development of finite amplitude sine wave into triangular wave.

We must hasten to add, however, that the simplicity of vibration simulation lies entirely in the test equipment, because as an environment, vibration is much more complex than the acoustic environment we have just discussed.

For example, a structural or equipment subassembly like the truss-spacecraft system in Fig. 16 is quite intimately attached to the ring frame-shroud structure. The dynamics (or impedances) of the attachment points are quite important in determining energy exchange. The dynamics of the truss system are, therefore, dependent on the *medium* (i.e., the ring frame) to which it is attached. This is in contrast to the dynamics of panels in energy exchange with a sound field. The air loading on the structure does not greatly alter the structural dynamics.

The simulation of a vibration environment as currently practiced can be exemplified by continuing to take the truss-spacecraft system as an example. Suppose that a measurement of ring frame acceleration in a direction normal to the shroud spectrum was obtained from a similar vehicle that had the spectrum shown in Fig. 10. We have decided that curve B should be the test spectrum, a shaker is attached to the foot of one of the trusses, and the test spectrum is maintained at that position. If the motion at the application point is controlled, however, the natural modes of the truss are those of a structure with the excitation point supported, which is an alteration of the system. We cannot avoid this by monitoring the force in the service vehicle and applying a given force [88] because then the truss modes are those of an unsupported or free system.

We may try to avoid this dilemma by attaching the trusses to a fixture (which may be similar to the ring frame) and shaking the fixture with a controlled acceleration. Unfortunately, the fixture may have one or several resonances in the frequency range of interest that change the acceleration spectra. These may be removed electrically by employing notch filters [89] or mechanically, by stiffening the fixture. In either case, however, the dynamics of the system has been substantially altered from the original system, with attendant complications in mechanical design of the text and signal processing.

Scharton has pointed out recently [90] that it may be possible to avoid some of the difficulties of the test fixture by replacing it with a light and flexible structure—a *multi-modal* test fixture. The large number of modes in the fixture would tend to smooth out the acceleration spectrum, and its panel-like character would tend to simulate the structural interactions between the truss and ring frame-shroud more accurately. This approach appears to have considerable merit, but more work needs to be done to prove its feasibility in general test procedures.

Aerodynamic Simulation

The testing of a vehicle for aerodynamic loads (in distinction to determination of loads) is difficult to do by direct simulation. If simulation is attempted in a wind tunnel, several problems occur. First, very few wind tunnels are large enough to accommodate vehicles of interest. Second, the large amount of acoustic noise existing in most tunnels interferes with the interpretation of response to aerodynamic loads. Finally, wind tunnel operation and logistics are very expensive and complicated compared to the acoustic and vibration facilities we have discussed.

In at least one case, aerodynamic simulation of loads has been shown to be feasible. In a study of the excitation of a flight vehicle by a turbulent boundary layer, Lyon has shown that it should be possible to simulate the resonant excitation of the structure by a suitable distribution of normally impinging jets, called wall jets. Each wall jet, in effect, behaves as a small broadband shaker. These are distributed over the structure in such a way that a fairly homogeneous vibration field is obtained. The spectrum is controlled by the nozzle diameter and volume flow of the jets. Details are given in Ref. 91.

4.4 Simulation by Environment Substitution

It often happens that one wishes to perform an environmental test using an environment different from the one being simulated. We might wish to avoid the difficulties just cited of aerodynamic simulation by exciting the structure with an *equivalent* sound field. Or, one may wish to replace an acoustic excitation by a source of mechanical vibration, either because one does not have the required acoustic facility or because the vibration test is judged more convenient. In this section, we explore the work that has gone on in substitution of loads, in particular examining the sense in which one load is equivalent to another.

Substitution of Acoustic for Aerodynamic Loads

The aerodynamic loads that one wishes to simulate are usually a TBL, separated flow, or oscillating shock. The spatial correlations for these fields are different from each other, and they are also different from that of a sound field. Thus, in general, to simulate the resonant structural response due to the TBL, we would require a sound field that had a different frequency spectrum from that of the TBL. We might also be interested in the sound generated within the structure by the TBL. Since the internal noise depends heavily on the transmission of energy by nonresonant modes (recall the discussion of shroud transmission in chapter 3), the differing spatial correlations mean that if the frequency spectra are adjusted to give the same resonant response spectrum for the two loads, then the nonresonant transmission will likely not be the same.

The establishment of an equivalent sound field for a given aerodynamic load will depend on the kind of response we are interested in and the nature of the structure. The equivalence may be established theoretically, as is done by Chandirami *et al.* [2] for launch vehicles, or it may be done empirically. To do the latter, one requires two pieces of information: (a) field data which relate TBL loads to the desired response, and (b) a second (perhaps laboratory) study which relates an external sound field to that same response. Neither of these fields need simulate the expected environment in amplitude or spectral shape, although clearly the same frequency range must be covered. Once the expected TBL spectrum is known, it is converted to a desired response spectrum. This expected response spectrum is then converted to an acoustic test spectrum using the acoustic excitation response transfer function that was experimentally developed.

As an example of the foregoing, suppose we are asked to test the spacecraft shown in Fig. 16 for its response during the transonic portion of its flight profile. Figure 27 shows the acoustic levels measured external to and within the shroud at launch [92]. The difference in these is the acoustic noise reduction (NR) of the shroud and is shown in Fig. 28.

In Fig. 29, we show the sound levels measured within the shroud during the shroud during the transonic portion of flight. If the spacecraft is the object to be tested, then these levels alone would be sufficient for testing purposes, since they could be applied directly to the payload. If the overall shroud-spacecraft system is of concern, however, then the NR previously obtained should be added to the internal levels to generate an equivalent acoustic test spectrum for the transonic flight regime. This *test* curve is also shown in Fig. 29.

Equivalence between Sound and Vibration

There are many reasons why one might wish to replace a specified acoustic test with a vibration test, and vice versa. The one most frequently cited is availability of test facilities, but cost, convenience, and ability to analyze the results are also considerations. Many aspects of the substitution problem are still in the research phase. Consider cost, for example. It is probably less

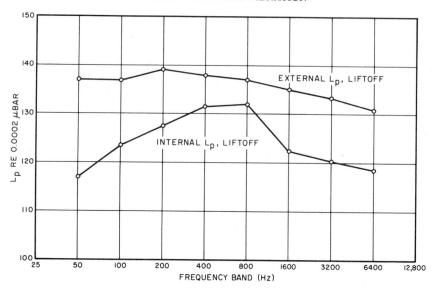

Fig. 27. Sound pressure levels measured external to and within a spacecraft shroud.

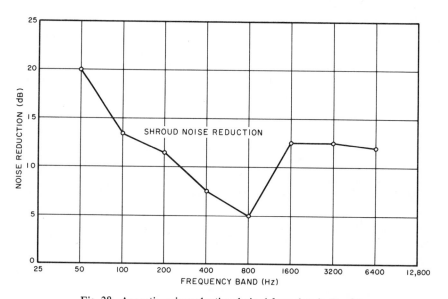

Fig. 28. Acoustic noise reduction derived from data in Fig. 27.

expensive to generate 10^3 watts of power into an acoustic wave than it is to develop the same mechanical power from a shaker. In an environmental test, however, only a small fraction of the acoustic power is absorbed by the structure from the sound field. Thus, the cost per watt of power into the structure may well be less from the shaker.

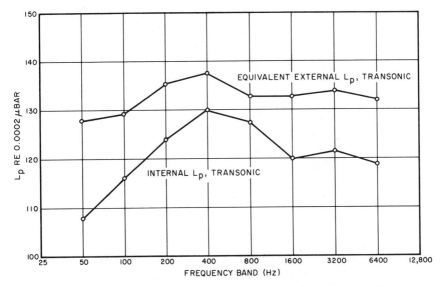

Fig. 29. Measured transonic levels within shroud and derived external *equivalent* L_p.

The most comprehensive effort to date on the replacement of acoustic excitation by mechanical shakers is the work of Noiseux [10]. By running a series of laboratory tests on the airborne computer shown in Fig. 30, Noiseux was able to show that in certain frequency bands the excitation of circuit boards was due to the acoustic environment, and in others it was due to the vibration at the mounting feet positions shown in Fig. 30. The combined environment was then simulated in a vibration test by requiring that the circuit board have its antic-ipated vibration levels. A comparison between realized and expected vibration levels on the circuit board is shown in Fig. 31.

A major difference between acoustic and mechanical excitation of extended structures is the greater spatial homogeneity of the acoustic excitation. To model acoustic excitation with vibration, therefore, we must (a) use many shakers, distributed over the structure; (b) excite an intermediate structure (a fixture) with the shaker and let it distribute the mechanical energy over the test struc-ture; (c) rely on the reverberation to diffuse the vibrational energy over the structure, or (d) some combination of these.

As an example of this, suppose we are interested in the transmission of vibra-tion to the spacecraft shown in Fig. 16 along its mounting truss due to acoustic excitation of the shroud. We may, however, elect to excite the shroud with a shaker rather than a sound field, in part to minimize the acoustic transmission to the spacecraft through the interior volume. (A shaker will produce less sound transmission due to nonresonant vibration than will the sound field [7, Fig. 14]. We may want to give ourselves some insurance in this regard also by placing some absorption in the interior volume.)

Fig. 30. Airborne computer in test configurations for acoustic and vibration response studies [93]: (a) typical arrangement for acoustic tests in reverberant room (note reference microphone); and (b) shock mount excitation in y-axis.

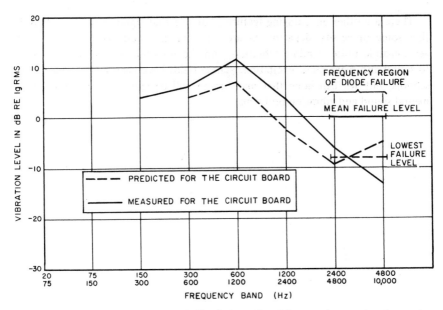

Fig. 31. Comparison of circuit board vibrations predicted from environment and response studies with levels measured during test firing [10].

There may be some inhomogeneity in the vibration field near the shaker, due to its *direct* field. The extent and magnitude of this direct field is dependent on the damping of the shroud and on the internal mechanical impedance of the shaker as compared to the point input impedance of the shroud. These factors are discussed very thoroughly in Ref. 94. The important fact for the present discussion is that the point of attachment of the shaker(s) to the shroud should be sufficiently removed from the ring frame so that the ring frame is exposed to a fairly homogeneous reverberant vibrational field in direct simulation of its condition under acoustic and aerodynamic excitation.

Closure

There are several encouraging features of the present patterns of development in sound and vibration environmental studies. One is the attempt to gather much more environmental data. Such data are essential, both for developing empirical and semi-empirical prediction schemes and for correlation with predictions using rational schemes of estimation.

A second feature that is encouraging is the attempt by environmental testing groups to develop and use their tests for evaluation of excitation and response parameters, i.e., to engage in relatively more *analytic* testing as compared to simple proof testing. This is in part motivated by a desire to reduce or modify test specifications, but it represents a desirable trend toward seeking better understanding of the system dynamics.

There are other encouraging features, but one that stands out particularly is that some university departments are now training students in the fields of aerodynamic noise, random vibration, and the response of complex structures to sound and mechanical excitation. These fields have been badly neglected in schools, but we can hope that many more will develop activities in environmental sound and vibration problems.

APPENDIX A
DEFINITION OF SYMBOLS

A	Intercept of pressure-acceleration level correlation
A_t	Turbulence correlation area
a	Skin acceleration
a	Vehicle radius
BPF	Base pressure fluctuations
C_{prms}	Fluctuation pressure coefficient
c	Sound speed in medium
c_ℓ	Longitudinal wave speed in structural material
D	Jet nozzle diameter
D	PSD of white noise process
E_a	Total energy of system a
f	Frequency
f_o	Resonance frequency of resonator
f_{osc}	Center frequency of oscillatory shock motion
f_r	Ring frequency of cylindrical vehicle
h_M	Modal impulse response
j_{MN}^2	Joint acceptance of modes
K	Scale factor
k	Acoustic wave number
k	Boltzmann's constant
k_1	Wave number, conjugate to x_1
L	Distance from downstream vehicle flare to oscillating shock
L	Elastic restoring force operator
L_a	Acceleration level (dB re 1 g)
L_p	Fluctuating pressure level (dB re 0.0002 μbar)
L_w	Acoustic power level (dB re 10^{-12} watt)
L_3	Correlation scale in cross-flow direction
M	Mach number, U/c
M	Resonator mass
M	Slope of pressure-acceleration level correlation
M_a	Mass of system a
n	Modal density
$P(\ )$	Pressure cross—PSD

61

P_{ind}	Pressure in induction field
P_M	Pressure amplitude in modal expansion
p_{ref}	Reference pressure, 0.0002 μbar
p_{rms}	Rms of fluctuating pressure
PSD	Power spectral density
$p(x, t)$	Fluctuating pressure
q	Dynamic pressure, $(1/2)\rho U^2$
R_N	Reynolds number per foot
R_{rad}	Radiation resistance
r	Radial coordinate
SEA	Statistical energy analysis
$S(f)$	PSD of random force applied to resonator
$S_p(f)$	PSD of pressure excitation
T	Absolute temperature
TBL	Turbulent boundary layer
t	Temporal coordinate
U	Jet efflux speed
U_c	Convection speed
V	Acoustic volume
V	Forward speed of vehicle
W	Structural surface density (lb/sq ft)
W_M	Displacement amplitude in modal expansion
w	System displacement
x	Spatial coordinate
x_c	Distance to shock formed by high-intensity sound wave
Y_M	Modal admittance function
a	Angle of attack of vehicle
β	Coupling factor relating pressure to modal force in Eldred's procedure
β	Viscous damping parameter
Δ	Frequency bandwidth
ΔP	Pressure jump across shock
δ^*	Boundary layer displacement thickness
$\delta(\ )$	Dirac delta function
δ_{MN}	Kronecker delta
η	Damping loss factor
η_a	Damping loss factor of system a
$\eta_{a,b}$	Coupling loss factor
θ	Eddy lifetime in turbulence

λ_a	Acoustic wavelength
λ_ℓ	Longitudinal wavelength in structure material
ξ_1, ξ_3	Spatial separation in downstream and transverse directions
Π_a^{diss}	Power dissipated in system a
$\Pi_{a,b}$	Power flow from system a to system b
$\Pi_{a,b}^{NR}$	Power flow from system a to system b by nonresonant motion of intervening system
Π_{rad}	Radiated sound power
ρ	Fluid density
ρ	Structural mass density
τ	Time delay
ϕ_m	"Moving axis" temporal correlation
ϕ_p	Space-time pressure correlation
ϕ_1	Downstream space-time correlation
ϕ_3	Cross-stream spatial correlation
ψ_M	Modal shape function
ω_M	Undamped modal resonance frequency
ω_M'	Damped modal resonance frequency
$\langle \ldots \rangle$	Averaging operator

APPENDIX B
BIBLIOGRAPHY

1. L. D. Landau and E. M. Lifshitz, *Fluid Mechanics*, Ch. 2, Addison-Wesley, Reading Mass., 1959.

2. K. L. Chandiramani *et al.*, "Structural Response to Inflight Acoustic and Aerodynamic Environments," BBN Rept. 1417, submitted June 1966 to NASA Marshall Space Flight Center, Huntsville, Ala., to be issued as Contractor's Report.

3. R. W. Mustain, "Dynamic Environments of the S-IV and S-IVB Saturn Vehicles," *Shock and Vibration Bull. No. 33*, Pt. 2, 72-88 (Feb. 1964).

4. A. Powell, "On the Fatigue Failure of Structures Due to Vibrations Excited by Random Pressure Fields," *J. Acoust. Soc. Am.*, 30, 1130 (1958).

5. An example of this process in specifying turbulent boundary layer pressure fluctuations is given by J. E. Ffowcs Williams and R. H. Lyon, "The Sound Radiated from Turbulent Flow Near Flexible Boundaries," BBN Rept. 1054, p. 12, submitted to ONR August 1963, N63-22525.

6. R. H. Lyon, "Empirical Evidence for Nonlinearity and Directions for Further Work," *J. Acoustic Soc. Am.*, 35, 1712 (1963).

7. J. E. Manning *et al.*, "The Transmission of Sound and Vibration to a Shroud-Enclosed Spacecraft," BBN Rept. 1431, submitted October 1966 to NASA Goddard Space Flight Center, Greenbelt, Md., to be issued as Contractor's Report.

8. R. H. Lyon, "Noise Reduction of Rectangular Enclosures with One Flexible Wall," *J. Acoust. Soc. Am.*, 35, 1791 (1963).

9. C. M. Ailman, "Wind Tunnel Investigations of the Fluctuating Pressures at the Surface of 2.75% Saturn Models," in *Acoustical Fatigue in Aerospace Structures* (W. J. Trapp and D. M. Forney, Jr., eds.), Syracuse Univ. Press, Binghamton, N.Y., 1965.

10. D. U. Noiseux, "Simulation of Reverberant Acoustic Testing by a Vibration Shaker," *Shock and Vibration Bull. No. 33*, Pt. 3, 125-136 (March 1964).

11. R. H. Lyon, "Boundary Layer Noise Response Simulation with a Sound Field," pp. 213-224 in *Acoustical Fatigue in Aerospace Structures* (W. J. Trapp and D. M. Forney, Jr., eds.), Syracuse Univ. Press, Binghamton, N.Y., 1965.

12. W. V. Morgan *et al.*, "The Use of Acoustic Scale Models for Investigating Near Field Noise of Jet and Rocket Engines," WADD Tech. Rept. 61, p. 178, April 1961.

13. H. E. von Gierke, "Aircraft Noise Control," Ch. 34 in *Handbook of Noise Control* (Cyril Harris, ed.), McGraw-Hill, New York, 1957.

14. J. P. Nenni and G. L. Gluyas, "Aerodynamic Design and Analysis of an LFC (Laminar Flow Control) Surface," *Aeronautics and Astronautics*, 52 (July 1966).

15. L. L. Beranek, "Criteria for Noise and Vibration in Buildings and Vehicles," Ch. 20 in *Noise Reduction* (L. L. Beranek, ed.), McGraw-Hill, New York, 1960.

16. P. A. Franken, "Jet Noise," Ch. 24 in *Noise Reduction* (L. L. Beranek, ed.), McGraw-Hill, New York, 1960.

17. B. L. Clarkson, "Scaling of Near Field Pressure Correlation Patterns Around a Jet Exhaust," Ch. 1 in *Acoustical Fatigue in Aerospace Structures* (W. J. Trapp and D. M. Forney, Jr., eds.), Syracuse Univ. Press, Binghamton, N.Y., 1965.

18. W. W. Willmarth and C. E. Wooldridge, "Measurements of the Fluctuating Pressure at the Wall Beneath a Thick Turbulent Boundary Layer," Univ. of Michigan Rept. 02920-1-T, Contract Nonr. 1224(30), April 1962, N62-12149.

19. I. Dyer, "Estimation of Sound-Induced Missile Vibration," Ch. 9 in *Random Vibration* (S. H. Crandall, ed.), John Wiley and Sons, New York, 1958.

20. D. A. Bies and P. A. Franken, "Notes on Scaling Jet and Exhaust Noise," *J. Acoust. Soc. Am.,* 33, 1171-1173 (1961).

21. P. A. Franken and F. M. Wiener, "Estimation of Noise Levels at the Surface of a Rocket-Powered Vehicle," *Shock and Vibration Bull. No. 31,* Pt. 3, 27-31 (April 1963).

22. D. A. Bies, "A Review of Flight and Wind Tunnel Measurements of Boundary Layer Pressure Fluctuations and Induced Structural Response," BBN Rept. 1269, 1966, NASA CR-626.

23. K. L. Chandiramani, "Interpretation of Wall Pressure Measurements Under a Turbulent Boundary Layer," BBN Rept. 1310, Sect. 2, Aug. 25, 1965, N66-12028.

24. R. H. Kraichnan, "Pressure Fluctuations in Turbulent Flow Over a Flat Plate," *J. Acoust. Soc. Am.,* 28, 378 (1956).

25. A notable exception is the work of L. Maestrello, "Test Results from the Boundary Layer Facility," Boeing Co. Rept. D6-9964, Vol. 3, May 1966. Copies of this report are not generally available, and the author should be contacted for information.

26. J. E. Ffowcs Williams, "On Convected Turbulence and Its Relation to Near Field Pressure," Univ. of Southampton (England) U.S.S.S. Rept. 109, Sect. 3, June 1960.

27. T. H. Hodgson, "Pressure Fluctuations in Shear Flow Turbulence," Ph.D. thesis, College of Aeronautics, Cranfield, England, Note 129, 1962.

28. L. Maestrello, "Measurement of Noise Radiated by Boundary Layer Excited Panels," *J. Sound Vib.,* 2 (2), 100-115 (1965).

29. F. J. Leech and V. E. Sackschewsky, "Boundary Layer Noise Measurements of the F-102 Aircraft," Rept. MRL-TDR-62-71, Aug. 1962.

30. W. H. Mayes, D. A. Hilton and C. A. Hardesty, "In-Flight Noise Measurements for Three Project Mercury Vehicles," NASA Tech. Note D-997, Jan. 1962, N62-10083.

31. D. A. Hilton, "In-Flight Aerodynamic Noise Measurements on a Scout Launch Vehicle," NASA Tech. Note D-1818, July 1963.

32. F. A. Smith and F. J. Benedetti, "Prediction of Re-entry Vibration," *Shock and Vibration Bull. No. 35,* Pt. 7, 9-18 (April 1966).

33. E. J. Richards and F. J. Fahy, "Turbulent Boundary Layer Pressure Fluctuations over Two-Dimensional Surfaces and Narrow Delta Wings," p. 47, Ch. 2 in *Acoustical Fatigue in Aerospace Structures* (W. J. Trapp and D. M. Forney, Jr., eds.), Syracuse Univ. Press, Binghamton, N. Y., 1965.

34. K. McK. Eldred, "Base Pressure Fluctuations," *J. Acoust. Soc. Am.,* 33 (1), 59-63 (1961).

35. G. W. Jones and J. T. Foughner, "Investigation of Buffet Pressures on Models of Large Manned Launch Vehicle Configurations," NASA Tech. Note D-1633, 1963, N63-16289.

36. M. V. Lowson, "The Fluctuating Pressures Due to Shock Interactions with Turbulence and Sound," Wyle Labs. Rept. WR66-35, June 1966.

37. A. L. Kistler, "Surface Pressure Fluctuations Produced by Attached and Separated Supersonic Boundary Layers," AGARD Rept. 458, 1963, N64-16663.

38. E. S. Rubin and E. M. Kerwin, "Experiments in Unsteady Aerodynamics Leading to the Development of an Acoustic Drag Coefficient," MIT Naval Supersonic Lab. Paper I-92, Tech. Rept. 179, presented at 9th Int. Cong. of Applied Mechanics, Brussels, Sept. 1956.

39. F. A. Teitzel *et al.,* "Time Histories of Ground Operations of B-52F and KC-135A Aircraft Engines," ASD-TDR-62-403, Jan. 1963.

40. P. T. Mahaffey and K. W. Smith, "A Method for Predicting Environmental Vibration Levels in Jet-Powered Vehicles," *Shock and Vibration Bull. No. 28,* Pt. 4, 1-14 (Aug. 1960).

41. P. A. Franken, "Sound-Induced Vibrations of Cylindrical Vehicles," *J. Acoust. Soc. Am.,* **34**, 453-454 (1962).

42. R. W. White, D. J. Bozich and K. McK. Eldred, "Empirical Correlation of Excitation Environment and Structural Parameters with Flight Vehicle Vibration Response," AFFDL-TR-64-160, Dec. 1964.

43. S. H. Crandall and W. D. Mark, *Random Vibration in Mechanical Systems,* Sect. 2.3, Academic Press, New York, 1963.

44. R. H. Lyon, "Propagation of Correlation Functions in Continuous Media," *J. Acoust. Soc. Am.,* **28** (1), 76 (1956).

45. G. Maidanik and R. H. Lyon, "Response of Strings to Random Noise Fields," *J. Acoust. Soc. Am.,* **28** (3), 391 (1956).

46. A. Powell, "On the Response of Structures to Random Pressures and to Jet Noise in Particular," Ch. 8 in *Random Vibration* (S. H. Crandall, ed.), Technology Press, Cambridge, Mass., 1958.

47. I. Dyer, "Response of Plates to a Decaying and Convecting Random Pressure Field," *J. Acoust. Soc. Am.,* **31** (7), 922 (1959).

48. H. S. Ribner, "Boundary-Layer-Induced Noise in the Interior of Aircraft," Univ. of Toronto UTIA Rept. 37, April 1956.

49. M. G. Cottis, "Green's Function Technique in the Dynamics of a Finite Cylindrical Shell," *J. Acoust. Soc. Am.,* **37**, 31 (1965).

50. Y. K. Lin, "Free Vibration of Continuous Skin-Stringer Panels," *J. Appl. Mech.,* **27**, 669-676 (1960).

51. Y. K. Lin, "Stresses in Continuous Skin-Stiffener Panels Under Random Loading," *J. Aerospace Sci.,* **29**, 67-75 (1962).

52. P. W. Smith Jr., "Resonances of a Periodically Supported Beam and Its Coupling to Sound," BBN Rept. 976, submitted to NASA Feb. 28, 1963.

53. C. A. Mercer, "Response of a Multi-Supported Beam to a Random Pressure Field," *J. Sound Vib.,* **2** (3), 293-306 (1965).

54. R. H. Lyon and G. Maidanik, "Statistical Methods in Vibration Analysis," *AIAA J.,* **2** (6) (June 1964).

55. F. K. Richtymyer and E. H. Kennard, *Introduction to Modern Physics,* Ch. 5, McGraw-Hill, New York, 1947.

56. E. A. Guillemin, *Introductory Circuit Theory,* Ch. 5, John Wiley and Sons, New York, 1953.

57. A. Powell, "Comments on the Response of a String to Random Distributed Forces," *J. Acoust. Soc. Am.,* **30**, 365 (1958).

58. A. Powell, "On the Approximation to the 'Infinite' Solution by the Method of Normal Modes for Random Vibration," *J. Acoust. Soc. Am.,* **30** (12) 1136-1139 (1958).

59. E. Skudrzyk, "Vibration of a System with a Finite or an Infinite Number of Resonances," *J. Acoust. Soc. Am.,* **30** (12), 1140-1152 (1958).

60. G. R. Corcos and H. W. Liepmann, "On the Contribution of Turbulent Boundary Layers to the Noise Inside a Fuselage," NACA Tech. Memo TM-1420, 1958.

61. P. W. Smith, Jr., "Response and Radiation of Structural Modes Excited by Sound," *J. Acoust. Soc. Am.,* **34** (5), 640 (1962).

62. R. H. Lyon and G. Maidanik, "Power Flow Between Linearly Coupled Oscillators," *J. Acoust. Soc. Am.,* **34** (5), 623 (1962).

63. T. D. Scharton, "Random Vibration of Coupled Oscillators and Coupled Structures," Sc.D. thesis, MIT Dept. of Mechanical Engineering, 1965.

64. E. E. Ungar, "Fundamentals of Statistical Energy Analysis of Vibrating Systems," AFFDL-TR-66-52, April 1966, AD 637 504.

65. D. E. Newland, "Energy Sharing in the Random Vibration of Non-Linearly Coupled Modes," *J. Inst. Math. App.,* **1** (3), 199-207 (1965).

66. R. H. Lyon, "Sound Radiation from a Beam Attached to a Plate," *J. Acoust. Soc. Am.,* 34 (9), 1265 (1962).

67. G. Maidanik, "Response of Ribbed Panels to Reverberant Acoustic Fields," *J. Acoust. Soc. Am.,* 34 (6), 809 (1962).

68. J. E. Manning and G. Maidanik, "Radiation Properties of Cylindrical Shells," *J. Acoust. Soc. Am.,* 36 (Oct. 1964).

69. R. H. Lyon and E. Eichler, "Random Vibration of Connected Structures," *J. Acoust. Soc. Am.,* 36 (7), 1344 (1964).

70. R. H. Lyon, "Noise Reduction of Rectangular Enclosures with One Flexible Wall," *J. Acoust. Soc. Am.,* 35 (11), 1791 (1963).

71. E. Eichler, "Thermal Circuit Approach to Vibrations in Coupled Systems and the Noise Reduction of a Rectangular Box," *J. Acoust. Soc. Am.,* 37 (6), 995-1007 (1965).

72. P. H. White and A. Powell, "Transmission of Random Sound and Vibration Through a Rectangular Double Wall," *J. Acoust. Soc. Am.,* 40 (4), 821-832 (1966).

73. R. H. Lyon and T. D. Scharton, "Vibrational Energy Transmission in a Three-Element Structure," *J. Acoust. Soc. Am.,* 38 (2), 253-261 (1965).

74. M. Heckl, "Vibrations of Point-Driven Cylindrical Shells," *J. Acoust. Soc. Am.,* 34 (10, 1553 (1962).

75. V. V. Bolotin, "On the Density of the Distribution of Natural Frequencies of Thin Elastic Shells," *J. Appl. Math. Mech.,* 27 (2), 538-543; trans. from *Prikl. Mat. Mekh.,* 27 (2), 362-364 (1963).

76. L. L. Beranek, "The Transmission and Radiation of Acoustic Waves by Solid Structures," Ch. 13, Sect. 13.7 in *Noise Reduction* (L. L. Beranek, ed.), McGraw-Hill, New York, 1960.

77. R. H. Lyon and J. E. Manning, "Analytical Procedure for Determining Random Load Acting on a Spacecraft Due to a Primary Random Load Acting on an Exterior Structure," 2nd quarterly rept., Contract NAS 5-9601, Sept.-Nov. 1965.

78. C. I. Malme, C. M. Gogos, I. Dyer, and P. W. Smith, Jr., "Sonic Fatigue Resistance of Structural Designs," BBN Rept. 873, Contract AF 33(616)-6340, March 1961, AD 269 187.

79. R. H. Lyon *et al.,* "Low Frequency Noise Reduction of Spacecraft Structures," NASA Rept. CR-589, Ch. 6, Sept. 1966.

80. R. G. North and J. R. Stevenson, "Multiple Shaker Ground Vibration Test System Designed for XB-70A," *Shock and Vibration Bull. No. 36,* Pt. 3, 55-70 (Jan. 1967).

81. M. A. Heckl *et al.,* "New Approaches to Flight Vehicle Structural Vibration Analysis and Control," ASD-TDR-62-237, Feb. 1962, AD 290-798.

82. J. H. Ball *et al.,* "Study of a Sonic Load Recorder," ASD-TDR-62-165, Vol. 1, Nov. 1962, AD 295 464.

83. P. W. Smith, Jr., and C. I. Malme, "Sonic Fatigue Life Resistance by Siren Testing," ASD-TR-61-639, Sect. 7, May 1962, AD 278 173.

84. A. W. Kolb and O. R. Rogers, "The Aeronautical Systems Division Sonic Fatigue Facility," *Shock and Vibration Bull. No. 30,* Pt. 5, 37-50 (May 1962). An updated version of this report is being prepared by A. W. Kolb and O. Maurer as an AFFDL report.

85. Personal communications with personnel at Manned Spacecraft Center, Houston, Texas.

86. D. J. Bozich, "Laboratory Simulation of the Response of Structures Exposed to Intense Acoustic Environments," *J. Acoust. Soc. Am.,* 37 (6), 1197 (1965).

87. R. D. Fay, "Plane Sound Waves of Finite Amplitude," *J. Acoust. Soc. Am.,* 3, 222 (1931).

88. J. Heinrichs, "Feasibility of Force-Controlled Spacecraft Vibration Testing Using Notched Random Test Spectra," *Shock and Vibration Bull. No. 36,* Pt. 3, 15-26 (Jan. 1967).

89.   J. V. Otts and N. F. Hunter, "Reproduction of Complex and Random Waveforms at Various Points on a Test Item," *Shock and Vibration Bull. No. 36*, Pt. 3, 47-54 (Jan. 1967).

90.   "Comparison of Fixture and Spacecraft Vibration Tests of a Mariner Electronic Assembly," BBN Rept. 1384, p. 8, submitted to Jet Propulsion Lab., July 1966.

91.   R. H. Lyon *et al.,* "Aerodynamic Noise Simulation in Sonic Fatigue Facility," BBN Rept 1349, AFFDL-TR-66-112, April 1966.

92.   L. A. Williams and W. B. Tereniak, "Noise Level Measurements for Improved Delta, Atlas/Agena-D and TAT/Agena-D Launch Vehicles," *Shock and Vibration Bull. No. 36*, Pt. 7, 89-102 (Feb. 1967).

93.   D. U. Noiseux, "Measurement of Acoustic and Vibration Response of Atlas Guidance Computer," BBN Rept. 1010, submitted to Space Technology Labs., Inc., April 22, 1963. A summary of this report appears as Appendix VI of "Random Vibration Studies of Coupled Structures in Electronic Equipments," Vol. 2, ASD-TDR-63-205.

94.   R. H. Lyon *et al.,* "Studies of Random Vibration of Coupled Structures,"ASD-TDR-62-205, Appendix I, Nov. 1962.